Freed & Fierce

The 7 Untapped Essentials for LifeLong Eating
Disorder Recovery

Written by
Kara Holmes, RN, BSN, INHC

www.vitalitycoaching.org

Dedicated to:

Janet Preese. I love you, Mom.

A Special Gift to My Readers

Included with your book purchase is my *"7 Hacks for Learning to Eat Without Fear of Weight Gain"*. This guide will help you take action, get organized, and feel empowered as you begin your recovery!

Get your free copy at 'bonusguide.vitalitycoaching.org'

Table of Contents

Introduction

After living with my eating disorder for 11 years and dropping out of therapy twice, recovery seemed completely unattainable for me. I never imagined that a year on, I would have pulled myself out of that dark space, that I'd be in full remission. I certainly didn't imagine that I would have transitioned from working as a full-time Registered Nurse to a Holistic Eating Disorder Recovery Coach, helping other women who are struggling with their eating disorders, as I once was, to find true healing.

It pains me that I was stuck in an unhealthy pattern with food, eating, and hating my body for so many years. Those years were precious, valuable time that was spent feeling trapped, depressed, guilty, and in a vicious cycle of self-hatred. But my struggle was not in vain. I was forced to find out, by myself, what was missing from therapy for me. What I learned in the years after dropping out of therapy was crucial to my own recovery. The beauty of this is that now I can share it with others, like you, and that is exactly why I have written this book.

While therapy helped me with some aspects of recovery, what really set me free and allowed me to recover is what I teach in my books and in my coaching practice. It was only through finding true balance in all areas of my life, and inviting God into each experience, that I was able to fully recover. That is why I advocate for a holistic approach to eating disorder recovery, and this is what you will discover inside this book.

Imagine how it would feel to be able to:

- Eat what you love without fearing that you might lose control.

- Be able to eat proper meals and still maintain a healthy weight.

- Feel good about your body and your appearance.

- Feel energized, optimistic and enthusiastic about life again!

It may not seem like you are capable of experiencing these things if you have also tried everything you can think of to recover! But remember, the insights that I am sharing with you came from having tried everything and failed. You won't find the content inside this book anywhere else because it comes from my own lived experience of my eating disorder and recovery process.

As you work through this book at your own pace, you will learn to quiet your eating disorder thoughts and stop thinking about food and how your body looks 24/7. You will learn how to eat without fear of gaining weight and how to stop engaging in restrictive eating behaviors, binging, and purging. Most importantly, you will learn to be at peace with yourself and to be happy with your body as it is. You'll rebuild your perspective of yourself and learn to feel beautiful and confident in your skin instead of assigning value to yourself based on societal ideals, or on what numbers you see on the scale.

I am so stoked about sharing my recovery process with you and about walking side by side with you on your journey as you heal and take steps towards building a more fulfilling, rewarding, and balanced life.

A Note on How to Read This Book

This book has been arranged in a very specific and purposeful way, so please read each chapter throughout the book in order. I know it can be tempting to skip ahead, but don't do that with this book!

The first few chapters of this book are dedicated to laying the groundwork, to getting your mindset in the right place for recovery so that you don't crash and burn doing things in an order that maybe could work, but is more likely to be a long road. I suggest that you also take your time reading each chapter and applying what you have learned. We are aiming for a slow, steady, lifelong recovery and not a 'quick-fix solution: one step at a time. If you 'slip-up,' remember to be kind, compassionate, and forgiving with yourself, and to keep pushing ahead. You have not failed: to fail means to stop trying completely.

It's also important to note that while I never intend for any content in this book to trigger anyone, it's possible that the mention of certain stories and behaviors may trigger thoughts or actions for you. I say this out of love, consideration, and respect for your journey. During the years I was my sickest mentally and physically, I read a handful of eating disorder recovery books. Some of the stories included were raw, unfiltered and vivid. It made me feel shocked and uncomfortable. By no fault of the authors, I felt triggered and I took that discomfort and engaged in eating disorder behaviors to try and wash the feeling away. This book will provide techniques to help you use more constructive behaviors when you feel uncomfortable, so there's that to look forward to!

Throughout the book, there will be many different practical activities and strategies for you to try out. For these, you will need a notebook and pen, so make sure to keep both handy!

The ultimate purpose of this book is to instill in you excitement, hope, and help you feel strong, fierce, and empowered to do the hard, yet rewarding, things. I want you to just 'know' with every fiber of your being that you can recover (even if you've already tried "everything"), and that you have a beautiful, vibrant life awaiting! I cannot wait for you to experience this joy that I once felt after coming from years of a perpetual place of darkness. Are you ready? Fair warning: transformation is ahead!

Chapter 1

The Psychology of Eating Disorders - Why Some People Develop Them and Others Don't

I'm going to guess that if you've picked up this book and have made it to this point, then somewhere along the line, either you or someone who cares deeply about you, have recognized your eating patterns as problematic.

The tough thing is, that even if you acknowledge that you have a problem, educating yourself about it can be, quite frankly...frightening! It's hard to stare your eating disorder in the face, and to be honest about the havoc it has wreaked on your life. What's even harder to imagine, is what your future might look like if you continue on this path of self-destruction.

As tough as it may be, learning about your eating disorder, especially why it may have developed and how it is maintained, does two crucial things.

You see, when you understand the roots of your eating disorder, suddenly, the pathways to recovery are illuminated. You begin to look at recovery with fresh eyes, and a renewed sense of hope, that what once seemed impossible, is indeed possible!

What is an Eating Disorder?

An eating disorder is a serious mental health condition that affects up to 9% of the population in the United States.[1]

Eating disorders are characterized by a preoccupation with body weight, shape, and size, and are accompanied by poor body image and low self-esteem. Attempts to control body weight, shape, and size become extreme in an abnormal way and present as disordered eating patterns and behaviors. The consequences of disordered

---

[1] See The National Association of Anorexia Nervosa and Associated Disorders for more Eating Disorder statistics.

eating extend beyond just the mental, and can cause serious damage to the body.

Some disordered eating behaviors, such as intentionally restricting food intake, can lead to a myriad of health issues, and it's not that difficult to see why. When you starve your body of essential, life-sustaining nutrients, your body responds by slowly shutting down. Without proper fuel, your body goes into 'survival' mode, and stops functioning the way that a healthy, happy body should! You may notice, if you have been restricting your food, or cutting out certain food groups for some time, that you struggle with one or more of the following: dry, brittle hair and nails; hair loss; low energy; poor memory and concentration; fainting; irregular menstrual periods, or amenorrhea; weakened bones; and heart palpitations.[2]

Other eating disorder behaviors, such as chronic, intentional vomiting, also known as purging food, can also lead to serious health issues. When you consistently purge food in this way, you are not just losing vital nutrients. You are also damaging your teeth, esophagus, stomach, and the

---

[2] See Kaye (2021) for more information on health implications related to eating disorders.

rest of the digestive system. This is due to a combination of the physical act of throwing up food and bringing up potent stomach acid. In time, stomach acid has the potential to erode your teeth and cause gum disease, and chronic vomiting can harm the stomach lining, causing ulcers, and can even lead to rupturing of the stomach and esophagus.[2]

While this all sounds absolutely horrible, the silver lining is that most, if not all of the ill-effects caused by eating disorders are reversible! There is still time to reverse these and other side effects when you commit to treating your body with the love and nourishment that it truly deserves.

Types of Eating Disorders

The three most common types of eating disorders are Anorexia Nervosa, Bulimia Nervosa, and Binge-Eating Disorder. Those with Anorexia Nervosa restrict their food intake, which in extreme cases, can lead to emaciation and malnourishment requiring urgent hospitalization and tube-feeding to prevent total organ failure. Those with Bulimia Nervosa engage in binge-eating behaviors, which are defined as consuming more than most people would consume in a specified time. Binge-eating in Bulimia

Nervosa is accompanied by purging behaviors, which consist of throwing up food, or laxative use. Bulimia Nervosa can also be accompanied by non-purging behaviors, which include ways to compensate for binge-eating without throwing up food. Examples include over-exercising and fasting. In Binge-Eating Disorder, binge-eating is present without the compensatory behaviors seen in Bulimia Nervosa.

Perhaps your symptoms don't quite resonate with any of those mentioned in these three eating disorders, but you or others have noticed some 'red flags' when it comes to your eating behaviors. In this case, you might still be experiencing an eating disorder, or be vulnerable to developing one. Some dysfunctional eating patterns have not been formally classified as eating disorders, but fall under the category 'Other Specified Feeding or Eating Disorders.'[3] What is important is that, if your eating behaviors are causing you distress, have become harmful, and are affecting your quality of life, then you likely need help and support.

---

3 See the National Eating Disorders Association for more information on what eating disorders are.

Eating Disorders: The Reality

The shocking reality of eating disorders is that they have the highest mortality rate of any mental illness, with 10,200 deaths a year. That is the equivalent of 1 death each hour [1]. Statistics also show that 26% of eating disorder sufferers attempt suicide. [1] This is the difficult truth of eating disorders, and what is even more disconcerting is that the rate of relapse for Anorexia Nervosa is 36%, and for Bulimia Nervosa, it is 35%. [4]

These statistics speak to the complexity of eating disorders, and is why, in this book, and based on my own recovery experience, I advocate for a holistic approach to eating disorder recovery!

Throughout this book, I will be sharing my own struggles with recovery, and how I finally found freedom after my third attempt.

The seeds of my body-image issues were planted at a very young age, where from as young as about 8 years old, I watched and took notice of my mother's own

---

[4] See Picot Derrick (2019) for more information on relapse in eating disorders.

struggles with how her body looked. It would take me 13 years to finally act on my own body insecurities, and another 5 years before I sought treatment for what had become a food addiction.

My eating disorder started to become more pronounced when I began college and the stress started piling up: I was working, living in my aunt's basement, and studying towards my nursing degree. At this low point in my life, every day felt like a burden I had to bear. As ashamed as I am to admit it, the only thing that allowed me to decompress, and offered me comfort, was food. It became a ritual of mine to stop at 2-3 places on the way home, at the end of each day, to pick up food.

It was around this time that I started therapy for the first time, too. I knew it would be a challenge to heal while focusing on so much at once, but I thought to myself, "I am worth it, and this part of my life HAS to go." I started a treatment program, which did not require me to be hospitalized or to be admitted to an inpatient center. Part of me wished it had, so I would have had the accountability.

I dropped out when I became unable to pay the therapy bills. They were racking up, and between paying tuition, rent, and other living expenses, I was completely overstretched. I thought to myself, "I'll have to try this again when I am more on my feet." I felt so defeated, but also happy in a weird way, that I could turn back to the familiar to cope with life's stressors: Food, followed by a trip to the bathroom. I was so embarrassed about this. It was my deepest, darkest secret that I would only tell the people I trusted.

In 2016 I decided to head to therapy again. I was in a serious relationship and we were planning to get married. I knew that I wanted to heal this thing once and for all, and this time, I was a little more mentally and financially prepared. I went back to therapy, this time to a different facility. Like before, it was also outpatient, but this time it included consulting with a psychiatrist, a therapist, a physician's assistant, AND a dietician…I thought, "How could I fail this time?"

8 months in and I found myself on the highest dose of Prozac I'd been on, ever. Three times the amount I had been started on by my doctor the year prior. I had gained more weight from my bingeing habits, and poorly

managed stress, and had no self-control or seeming capability to shift my lifestyle and my behaviors. Why was it that I was failing therapy...again?

The bills were still over my financial means, and with a wedding to pay for and what seemed like no progress whatsoever, I dropped out again. I was not over it, but I was over this way of recovering.

Why wasn't it working for me?? I am a problem-solver and someone who never gives up, but at this point, I was praying for a miracle from God, but believing that I would always be stuck with this in some sort of way. I believed it would get better and then come back my entire life.

To my delight, I couldn't have been more wrong. In less than a year from dropping out, I had healed with complete remission for the first time.

Therapy wasn't the reason I didn't heal though. It just wasn't everything I needed. I needed more. Now I understand, and it's a holistic approach. I needed to look at each area, mind, body, and spirit, to heal completely. To be healed was the happiest moment of my life.

Throughout this book, I will be revealing this holistic approach to recovery and how it helped me to completely heal from my eating disorder. I will share just why I believe this approach is so important when it comes to relapse prevention and lifelong recovery.

Why Do Eating Disorders Happen?

Eating disorders, like other mental health issues, are complex, and their cause cannot be reduced to one single factor. What is usually found is that a multitude of factors works together to make someone more or less vulnerable to developing an eating disorder. If a person experiences a triggering event or a series of triggers, and enough risk factors are present, they may develop an eating disorder.

You may be curious about why some people develop eating disorders while others don't, despite apparent risk factors being present. Well, just as risk factors exist and can contribute to the development of mental illness, so do protective factors exist that can act to decrease these risks. Protective factors will play an important role later on when I introduce my *7 Pillars for Eating Disorder Recovery*.

The diagram below shows us what health professionals have called the 'Biopsychosocial Model' of mental health, and it is quite clear by looking at this diagram, that holistic mental health is influenced by a multitude of factors.[5] These are made up of (as the name suggests), biological, physical, social, and psychological aspects, which combined, contribute to the development of mental illness.

Figure 1

Applying this model to eating disorders, and starting at the physical and biological level, some research has found

5 See Engel (1977) for more on the Biopsychosocial Model of Health.

a genetic risk factor for eating disorders, for example, having a parent who had or has an eating disorder.[6] Other biologically-based risk factors could include going through puberty. During puberty, your body goes through drastic changes and you start to develop more bodily awareness. You may start to compare yourself with others, and become unhappy with how you look. This may lead you to feel uncomfortable in your new body, which was my experience.

I spent a couple years in high school praying for God to change my body. I used to ask him to please let me wake up taller and thinner. I wanted people to notice me for the way my body looked. I needed to have firm, thin legs. Instead, the reality is that I have a curvy figure, hips that I learned later were actually attractive to a lot of men. I didn't know that at the time.

Comments from others on your changing appearance can have a direct impact on how you view yourself, even years down the line. My mom rejected certain parts of herself in front of me, and my dad told me I had "a little extra on me" one night at the dinner table as I went for a second

---

[6] See Cedars (2021) for more information on how genetics influence the development of eating disorders.

helping of pasta. That was that. The decision was sealed. It was unacceptable to both of my parents to gain any weight or look a certain way. I felt like I couldn't let them down. I was going to have to do whatever it took to maintain that.

As far as psychological risk factors are concerned, the ones that stand out when it comes to eating disorders are those such as low self-esteem, body-image dissatisfaction, and perfectionism. The less obvious, that carry equal risk include those like perceived lack of control and emotional dysregulation.

In my case, my body-image issues stemmed partly through social learning, or learning through watching others. When I started to notice that my mom was often checking her body in the mirror, I never thought twice about it. Nor did I question the negative comments she made towards herself, and certain areas of her body that she felt ...were just not okay. I didn't know it at the time, but the seeds were planted. Because she was my role model. I learned that I couldn't look a certain way if I was going to be happy with my body.

This experience was difficult for me to share as I love my mother immensely, and I know that she didn't realize her own body-image issues would rub off on me. I do believe that it is important to share these experiences, though, because they are so common in people struggling with eating disorders. I don't want you to feel alone in your struggles. This is often how eating disorders make us feel - alone. They force us to keep our pain and shame hidden, keeping us isolated from our social networks, and keeping the disorder going!

You might be surprised to notice that perceived lack of control is a risk factor in eating disorders. This factor can be less obvious than the others and is more often something that could be beyond your awareness. However, going back to the nature of eating disorders, they are essentially about controlling, or a lack of control with weight, shape and size, as well as eating habits.

The Transdiagnostic Model of Eating Disorders[7] says that all eating disorders share common symptoms. According to the model, what underlies the development of all eating disorders is shaky self-esteem that depends largely on the over-evaluation of eating, shape, weight and their

---

7 See Vitousek & Brown (2015) to learn more about the Transdiagnostic Model of Eating Disorders.

control, together with the over-evaluation of achieving 'perfectionism.'[7]

That seems like a fair explanation, but the question that remains is, why do people with eating disorders feel this need to control? The reasons will, of course, be different according to each person's unique situation. Oftentimes, what we find is that something in a person's outer world is perceived as out of their control. Hence, the need to retain control. This certainly resonates with my own story.

My father controlled almost everything that I did, but at a distance. He worked long hours. When his truck rolled into the garage at the end of a long workday, a pit grew in my stomach. You could hear the conservative talk show host, Rush Limbaugh's voice, as we heard his vehicle door open. Dad would slam his heavy truck door. I could hear him complaining about any old thing - the cat in the driveway - kids walking across our grass again. Driving home took over an hour. It was always something. I knew not to ask him for permission to go anywhere or do anything I wanted to do as a teenager, because he would scoff at me, shake his head, and ignore me. He would walk across the room, back and forth, putting things away. He was silent, but anger brewed beneath the surface that you could feel in a thick cloud. I would ask again and the most common response was, "You don't need to do that. Just stay home," in an annoyed tone of voice. I was afraid of my dad. I didn't understand why he was so upset all of the time. It bothered me.

You can often draw similarities in the family dynamics of those who go on to develop eating disorders. In this case, you can see how perceived lack of control, and over-controlling behavior by parents can create the temptation in a young teenager exploring their independence, to want to control some aspect of their life. Another important risk factor that this story, and the next one draws attention to, is emotional dysregulation, and the conditions that prevent young people from developing the skills required to manage their own emotions.

My mom was the comforting, balancing force in my life. She guided my siblings and me through difficult emotions with dad and homeschooled us all into high school. At age 8, everything I knew was what my mom had taught me. In addition, I saw how my dad treated her. He yelled at her, criticizing her for what seemed like small things, and how she parented us while he was away at work all day. I saw her cry and ponder how she could do better. Often confused about how to keep dad happy, my siblings, my mom, and I shared a bond over that. I loved my dad too, but these interactions made me feel torn. He was our financial provider and I understood that. He took us on vacations and knew how to go camping. I loved when we could get a glimpse of him behind his anger during these family trips. I remember wishing I could have more leader-like nurturing from my dad when I was growing up.

This, and the previous story paint a picture of how, when you learn, as a very young child, that your parents' emotional needs are more important than your own, your instinct is to put your own needs aside. Also, when you see a parent expressing their emotions in a way that you can't make sense of (as with me and my dad), you can become confused and may come to associate emotional expression with something 'bad'. Ultimately, this all leads to the avoidance, mismanagement, or misdirection of your own emotions because you haven't learned the proper skills to cope with strong, or difficult emotions. This is what 'emotional dysregulation' means.

I believe that the pain of not being able to and even being scared to express yourself and your emotions, coupled with the shame surrounding this, is at the very core of eating disorders. The behaviors that you adopt are a way of managing and providing comfort for the extreme pain that you feel underneath the mask that you put on each and every day. The behaviors that you rely on bring not only relief but a sense of pleasure too, so much so that you can begin to depend on them. This dependence has been compared to dependence as it is understood in addictions[8] and speaks to why recovery can be so difficult in eating disorders, as well as why the rate of relapse is so high.

Social risk factors for eating disorders include such things as family environment, parental attitudes towards weight and appearance, and parents' own body-image issues. Most of these have already come up, where we discussed psychological risk factors. As represented in the previous diagram, there is a lot of overlap between psychological and social risk factors. Some other social risk factors may include bullying; peer-pressure and media pressure to be thin; societal ideals that value thinness; as well as trauma such as physical and sexual abuse.[9]

---

[8] See Ekern & Karges (2012) for more information on Eating Disorders and Addiction.

[9] See Ghaderi & Scott (2001) for more information on Eating Disorder Prevalence, Incidence and Risk Factors.

Identifying Your Own Disordered Patterns and Triggers: The Benefits of Enhanced Self Awareness.

At this point, you should have a fairly reasonable idea about what eating disorders are, and how they may be caused. You may have even started thinking about and recognizing some of these patterns as similar to what you experience. Building this self-awareness is an incredible first step.

As you also discovered though, eating disorders are highly complex. Although there is some overlap in symptoms and underlying causes, it's important to remember that your story is unique.

It is important, when starting your recovery, to get a good snapshot of your eating disorder. This means figuring out your triggers, as well as what feelings and behaviors are responsible for keeping your eating disorder going. The value of getting this 'snapshot,' is that, once you gain a better understanding of how your eating disorder functions, you can begin to out-smart it!

So, as a first active step in your recovery process, I'd like to challenge you to take your awareness further by having you try out a self-monitoring activity.

In this activity, you will use a sheet of paper or a journal to monitor and track your eating habits, exercise, as well as any compensatory behaviors that were mentioned earlier (purging, laxative use, and exercise). In addition to noting the frequency of these behaviors, you should also include information about what was going on (the situation) when you started eating, exercising, or engaging in compensatory behaviors (if relevant), as well as any thoughts and feelings that accompanied the situation. This will provide insight into your emotional and situational triggers.

It is important to monitor yourself daily for at least one week. You should monitor yourself in real-time, using timestamps. It is important to monitor yourself in real-time because if monitoring is not done accurately, you will not get the snapshot that you need. Often, when people try to think back on their behaviors, they tend to forget exactly what was going on at the time! But when it comes to monitoring your eating disorder, these details can be vitally important. By doing this, you'll be able to see patterns within your behavior, which could lead to a breakthrough in your own recovery process. For example, I began taking note of my binge-eating episodes over the holidays one year. I recognized that I was refraining from eating the entire day and "saving" my calories for the large meal at the planned gathering. This method set me up for a binge because my body wasn't getting the nutrients it needed regularly throughout the day. In each situation, I had been extremely hungry for hours, having put off eating in anticipation of a big meal. I would end up eating a lot more than was comfortable, usually bingeing and feeling sad.

Example of the Self-Monitoring in Disordered Eating Behaviors

Day:				Date:
Time	Setting	Food consumed	Compensatory Action	Situation/Thoughts/Feelings
7am	Home - on the couch in front of TV.	1 family pack Reese's miniature cups	Purged afterwards	Was supposed to meet my friend last night but she canceled at the last minute. Felt awful all night didn't sleep well, keep thinking "does she still like me, did I do something wrong?" Felt sad, lonely and defeated.

Table 2

Eating Disorder Recovery - Introduction to the 7 Pillar System

My hope is that by now, you are getting more and more eager to learn about what lifelong eating disorder recovery entails. I am beyond excited to share my unique and holistic recovery approach with you!

If you'll remember, when I introduced the Biopsychosocial Model of Mental Illness earlier, I spoke about how, while there are factors that increase the risk of developing an eating disorder, there are also factors that protect against the development of eating disorders.

This is incredible news for recovery! In the final part of this chapter, I am going to give you a hint at what you can expect from the *7 Pillar System for Sustained, life-long recovery*, which is based on a holistic approach to eating disorder recovery. This system draws on my own recovery experience, but is also backed by the science of what creates protective factors against the development of mental illness.

If we dive back into the risk factors that are associated with eating disorders, we can distinguish what some of the defensive factors might be. If having low self-esteem contributes to and maintains a disordered eating mentality, then how do you build up self-esteem? Self-esteem grows when you feel secure about yourself and your abilities: when you feel that you are a worthy and valuable human being. [10] Security within yourself comes from having developed a solid sense of self, that you feel confident about. You can only start to feel capable when you open yourself up to opportunities that make you feel accomplished. To feel worthy and valuable, you need to work on your core beliefs, which color your perception of yourself and of the world around you. You also need to learn how to take better care of yourself. It's easy to take on the stress of life and neglect parts of our lives that need our attention, which can make us suffer mentally and physically.

Having an eating disorder stops you from taking proper care of yourself. Instead of building yourself up, having an eating disorder mindset makes you hyper-critical. That's why, in recovery, you need to replace your harsh

---

[10] See Cherry & Morin (2021) for more information on Self-Esteem.

inner-dialogue with an accepting, compassionate, and kind voice.

Building up your self-esteem is just one piece of the puzzle. Another important protective factor is having the right tools, and sufficient tools in your self-care toolbox to cope with difficult emotions, and to manage everyday stressors in a healthy way. That means giving up your old habits of depending on food as a comfort, and relinquishing control of your disordered eating patterns. You need to make room for new habits, ones that are tried and tested, and that actually work!

In order to re-shape negative attitudes towards food and weight, especially holding a lot of fear around gaining weight and losing control, it requires you to learn about proper nutrition and feeding yourself in a loving way. If you understand the science behind how your body works, (not just how you gain weight) but also what makes you feel hungry and what makes you feel satisfied; as well as why optimal nutrition is crucial for you to function at your best, something marvelous happens! You begin to gain a new sense of appreciation for your body and the effortless ways in which it keeps you alive everyday. With this knowledge, you can begin to replace fear with possibilities, like the possibility that recovery doesn't need to be so scary, and that you won't lose control.

As you learned earlier, eating disorders are also maintained by keeping you isolated from your support system. You become solely reliant on the eating disorder to make you feel good, and to provide peace from any pain you may be feeling. It is a well-known fact in the psychology of mental illness, that social support is a huge protective factor against the development of mental illness,[11] and this is especially true when it comes to eating disorder recovery. It is so important to lean on others, and to find support through communities that can understand and relate to what you are experiencing.

Something else that eating disorders do, is that they rob you of finding meaning in any other aspect of your life. The sole purpose of your life revolves around food, trying to control your eating habits, and your weight, shape and size, to the complete detriment of everything else. A huge part of recovery then, has to do with finding new purpose and creating meaning in life outside of your eating disorder. This

---

[11] See Ozbay et al. (2007) for more information on Social Support and Resilience to Stress.

might be in work, in hobbies, in spirituality, or a combination of all three.

Keeping these protective factors in mind, and learning valuable lessons from my own eating disorder recovery journey, I have designed the **7 Pillar System for Eating Disorder Recovery**. I am beyond excited to reveal this holistic system with you as you work your way through this book!

Pillar I:

Mindset

Chapter 2

Why Mindset Matters in Eating Disorder Recovery

Did you know that mind power is a real thing? I'm not referring to the way in which a young girl was able to move physical objects through extreme concentration, using only her mind (if you've ever watched the movie Matilda, you'll get this reference!). The mind power that I am talking about is, fortunately, much easier to harness with consistent practice and the right attitude.

Wouldn't it be wonderful if I told you that it was possible to control what you think, how you feel, as well as how you react to different situations? Can you imagine what that would mean for your recovery?

It probably seems far-fetched right now because of how your eating disorder mind functions - I can hear those self-defeating thoughts because I have lived them! But I'm here to tell you, as somebody who has walked in your shoes, and who is now fully recovered...with 100% certainty, it IS possible. I have written this book confidently believing that it is completely possible for you too!

If changing your mindset was not possible, then imagine how many psychologists and coaches would be out of business. Mental health professionals are trained and equipped to help you shift your mindset, and there is a wealth of research out there on the topic of mindset, and how to adopt a positive mindset.

While I'm not a trained psychologist, I did learn a lot through my own experience in therapy, as well as through my own trial and error. That's why I feel confident sharing my insights with you. I am sharing what really helped me overcome obstacles to building a recovery mindset when my eating disorder was the most powerful force in my life.

First, I want you to better understand what I'm talking about when I use the term 'mindset.'

What is a Mindset?

You can think of your mindset as an amalgamation of all of the beliefs and attitudes you hold that influence the way you perceive and interact with the world.

Maybe you're thinking, "How did I end up with the mindset I have right now?" and maybe, to some extent, you're even thinking that it's not fair, that other people just don't experience the same problems that you do with your mindset. On some level, it is unfair...after all, it is our experiences and the environment that we grew up in that shapes our mindsets.

However, it's not all that bad, and research conducted on the malleability of mindsets has proven this[12]. Apparently, just knowing that your mindset is flexible can be enough to shift your thinking in a more positive direction, and to instill hope in the idea that you can turn your mindset around for the better[12]. Taking this a step further, studies that have analysed brain scans of people with major depression, before and after therapy, have shown that psychotherapy can

---

[12] See Crum et al. (2013) for more information on the role of mindset in stress management.

result in the "normalization of functional brain activity at a global level."[13] The proof is in the pudding!

Hopefully that's enough encouragement that you're feeling a bit more optimistic about the potential within you to change your mindset. Though you may face many challenges and obstacles along the way, it's okay, I'm in this with you for the long haul! I know that with my help, we can transform your mindset, one step at a time. Step by step, we will take your mindset from being dominated by disordered eating thoughts, merely surviving, going through the motions...to a fully recovered and thriving mindset, full of hope and enthusiasm for the future!

Reflecting on Your Current Mindset

Something that may be useful when it comes to changing your mindset, is to go back to the principle I spoke about in chapter one: awareness. Again, if you become aware of your core beliefs, attitudes, and perceptions about yourself and the world, you can use this self-knowledge to guide you in making necessary adjustments.

---

[13] See Beauregard (2014) pg.75 for more information on brain changes before and after therapy.

It can be difficult to just 'know' what your mindset is, though. Some of your beliefs, attitudes and perceptions lurk beneath the surface of conscious awareness. Luckily for you, though, I have just the right self-reflection tools that can help you access these!

First, let's try out the way of just trying to think about what your core beliefs, attitudes and perceptions may be by asking yourself the following questions:

1) What do you believe to be true about yourself?

   E.g. "I weigh too much", or "others can recover and be happy, but I can't."

2) What rules do you have about how you believe you should live your life? (think about times where you have told yourself "I should; I ought to; and I must").

   E.g. "I should make sure I don't gain any more weight."

3) What do you believe to be true about the world/others?

   E.g. People will like me more if I am thin and light enough.

Can't think of anything? Here is a prompt that might help you if you're feeling stuck:

Try to think back to the last time you felt a really strong, negative emotion. Got it? Okay, now look at the example below, and try to break it down using the approach that I have used.

Step 1.

Write out a short description of the situation that triggered a strong emotional response.

Situation: "It was my birthday and I spent it at home alone. My boyfriend had gone away on a business trip and asked me if I minded him being away. I said no, but I really did want him to stay. Nobody really made a big deal of it, and I only got a few calls during the evening."

Step 2.

Write out the immediate, automatic thoughts that came to your mind while in this situation.

Thoughts: "Clearly nobody cares about me, I'm not special enough, I'm obviously not a very likeable person."

Step 3.

Write out how you felt when you had these thoughts. Feelings: "I felt lonely and depressed."

Step 4.

Let's go back to your thoughts, which can help reveal your self-beliefs. If the thoughts you had were really true, what would that say about you? What would be so bad about that?

Self-beliefs: "If nobody cares about me, it means that I'm not worth caring about, and that would be bad because it means that I'm not worthy of being cared for and loved. That must mean I'm unworthy and unlovable."

Step 5:

Next, write down what actions you took in response to the situation:

Actions: "I ignored the calls that came through in the evening and I started to act cold and distant towards my boyfriend. I also had a food binge because I was feeling bad about myself, and worthless."

How do you feel after having completed this activity, using your own example? Do some self-reflection, and think about what you have learned about yourself.

The purpose of doing this activity is to help you understand how your mindset is driven by your core beliefs (those deeply held assumptions, like "others can recover and learn to be happy, but not me"), and to demonstrate how much power your mindset has in influencing your behaviors.

I'm going to take a bet about your next question, and guess that you're wondering something along the lines of: "How then, do I go about changing my core beliefs?"

The truth is, it takes a lot of practice, and consistent effort. You need to enhance your self-awareness: it's about catching yourself in those moments where your thoughts are on auto-pilot, and then challenging them right then and there. Ready to give it a try? You've got this!

Look again at my example above. I'm going to challenge my initial interpretation of the situation, and the way I thought about it:

"Although my boyfriend did go away over my birthday, the business trip was an important one that had been delayed for a while. I know he didn't do this because he didn't care about me, or to try and hurt me, otherwise he wouldn't have asked me if I was okay with it first. I know that it took my special people till evening time to call and wish me happy birthday, but I can appreciate the fact that my birthday fell on a weekday and that most of them work busy, full-time jobs and evening time is when they are more available for phone calls. The fact that they phoned me in the evening could also point to the fact that they wanted to call me at a time that would allow them to give me their undivided attention on my special day. I AM cared for and worthy of receiving love."

Can you see how interpreting the initial situation in this way might have led to different feelings and actions? Now, try to re-interpret the situation that YOU thought of. I expect that doing this activity would be difficult. After all, you are probably not used to talking to yourself in this way.

When you have an eating disorder, you become so accustomed to criticizing yourself, and talking down to yourself. That's why changing the language that has become so automatic and something you have known for maybe years, is so tough, and requires practice!

Psychologists who practice Cognitive Behavioral Therapy, refer to the 'mistakes' we make in our thinking as 'thought errors.' 'Thought errors' are, essentially, misinterpretations in the way we perceive events.[14] In fact, many 'thought errors' are so common that psychologists have actually compiled a list of them and labeled them. This is to make it easy for their clients to identify which 'errors' they typically make, and to improve awareness of them and how they are unhelpful.

I'll introduce a few of these here so that you, too, can get a basic idea of what these 'thinking errors' look like and how they are labeled. This will also help you to identify which ones, if any, you tend to make.

1. 'All or Nothing Thinking'

This is the tendency to interpret situations in black and white terms: you see something as either 'good' or 'bad,' with no in-between[13].

---

[14] See Jacobson (2019) for more information on 'Thought Errors.'

For example, say you score 80% on a test...because it is not your usual 90% or above, you interpret this grade as 'bad,' and you end up feeling like you have 'failed.'

2. Jumping to Conclusions

If you tend to jump to conclusions, it means that you often believe that you know what others are thinking or feeling towards you[13]. For example, your friend hasn't called you for a while so you assume she does not care about you. Jumping to conclusions can also present as thinking you will know what outcome will happen.

For example, you have a presentation coming up and you just 'know' you're going to make a fool out of yourself.

3. Overgeneralization

Overgeneralization happens when you have one bad experience, and then you make a conclusion about all future experiences based on that. For example, you go on one bad date and conclude that you will be single forever.[13]

4. Catastrophizing

When you catastrophize, it means that you imagine the worst possible outcome. For example, you make a mistake at work: say you sent out a meeting invite but it was for the wrong time. You may start thinking that because of this, you will lose your job, you won't be able to pay your expenses, and will end up homeless.[13]

5. Mental Filter

If you use mental filtering, it means that you tend to focus on the negative aspects of a situation only, and filter out any positive aspects. For example, say you had an idea at work that you shared with your colleagues: all but one of them disliked your idea.

If you use mental filtering, you would completely discount all the positive feedback regarding your idea and would only focus on the one negative response that you received. [13]

These are just a few examples of common 'thinking errors,' but there are many more. As you can see, thinking in these kinds of ways is unhelpful and doesn't serve you well.

Now, let's turn back to the reframing activity you completed earlier: you might find that...okay, you've completed the activity but what's the point if you don't believe in what you just wrote down anyway?

Don't worry about that right now, it doesn't mean that you have failed or that you have done the activity incorrectly. Talking to yourself in a different way, and believing in your new mindset will take time. Think of your mindset like a muscle in your body, that when you work out, gets stronger over time. You can also think of it like learning to tie your shoelaces as a kid - it probably took multiple tries but now it's second-nature! That is exactly what will begin to happen if you are patient and consistent with practicing your new mindset.

Why Changing Your Mindset is So Difficult

Because I've walked a journey similar to yours, I know that along your recovery process you will likely find it difficult to keep going, even after having made the decision and commitment to recover. It is human nature to be resistant to change, to want to stick with what's comfortable. When dealing with an eating disorder that functions to distract you from your 'real' problems and your 'real' pain, resistance comes into play. When you start your recovery, it's as if you're undergoing an operation, but you're not offered any anesthesia. That's why it's so hard - you are forced to confront the pain in its raw form!

The natural response will be to resist. You'll find that there are times when your eating disorder mind becomes incredibly noisy, trying relentlessly to get you to hold on to your old habits and ways of thinking, to block your progress. Your eating disorder will play on your fears and insecurities, which it knows all too well.

Remember what was said about awareness and about out-smarting your eating disorder? Having been through recovery, and being aware of the different tricks your eating disorder can play on your mind during the process, I'm going to share these with you. The aim being that you can go into your recovery journey prepared and ready for what to expect!

Fear is a huge barrier to recovery. When you try to recover, your fears about gaining weight and losing control will become that much stronger. For me, personally, I was stuck here for the longest time. As someone who suffered from Binge-Eating Disorder, and already being overweight,

I was terrified at the possibility of gaining even more weight during recovery. I can assure you, though, that when you follow a holistic approach to recovery, (which includes learning about nutrition, about how the body works, self-acceptance and nurturing each area of your life) these fears will eventually start to fade.

Your eating disorder will also play on your low self-esteem and your need for approval and acceptance. It will make you fear what others might think, it will make you fear being perceived as a failure, it will make you fear that people will see you for what you really believe about yourself at your core, whether deep down you believe that you are unworthy, unlovable, broken, or something else. When your defenses are stripped away (your eating disorder behaviors), you are left bare and exposed, and that can be a frightening thought. In time, though, you will come to think about yourself differently. You will start to believe a different, positive story about yourself that has been stifled by your eating disorder for a very long time.

Your eating disorder will also make you apprehensive about life after recovery, it will make you question whether things can really change for the better, whether you will really be happy without it. It will even make you wonder about whether you deserve to recover at all - it will break you down, and take you back to all those negative core beliefs that you hold about yourself. It will make you fear and doubt your own potential to get better, to rebuild your identity and discover your purpose outside of your preoccupation with food and your body.

I want you to know that you are more than your eating disorder, more than a label. In the next chapters, we will be focusing on bringing your authentic self out from hiding, and on revisiting your hopes and dreams for your future that your eating disorder has stolen from you.

Overcoming Obstacles to a Recovery Mindset

As you have just learned, your eating disorder wants to keep you stuck. That is exactly why preparing yourself for mental obstacles, like those that were discussed, ahead of time, is the best way to set yourself up for a successful recovery process. I'm going to share with you a strategy that you can use to work against your mental blocks, that is a little different from the one you learned earlier. This can be used as an emergency strategy at those times when it's difficult to quiet your eating disorder thoughts. Like the earlier one, the best way to use this strategy is to make it a regular practice!

This strategy involves creating what we call 'affirmations' and 'mantras'. Affirmations are phrases that you can tell yourself to reinforce the mindset that you want to adopt. If you look back to the previous activity, you will notice that when I reframed my interpretation of the situation, I stated at the end that "I am worthy of receiving love and being cared for." This is an affirmation because it affirms the way I want to feel, and what I want to believe, even if I don't fully believe it at the time.

Sometimes, as you may have recognized, it can be difficult to reframe your negative thinking patterns, especially when you just get started. That is why it is helpful to think of some affirmations in advance that you can fall back on, just in case you get stuck.

I'm going to get you to write out some affirmations about your eating disorder recovery for those 'stuck' times, but first, I want to share some golden rules about affirmations:

1. Affirmations should be written in the positive and in the present tense, as if they are already happening. This is

the type of language that our subconscious minds understand and respond to best.

E.g. "I am worthy."

2. If the word 'affirmation' doesn't resonate with you, you can utilize the word 'mantra' as an alternative as you create and use your phrase. A mantra is a phrase that is said out loud or internally and repeated during a spiritual practice, like in prayer or meditation.

3. Affirmations should be practiced out loud, while standing in front of a mirror, looking at yourself. You should confidently repeat your affirmations to your reflection staring back at you. This method is more intentional, enhances awareness, and makes affirmations even more powerful.

4. Affirmations should be practiced regularly, so that they eventually become more natural, and more deeply ingrained. Ideally, you want to set time aside to practice them daily, as part of a routine.

You can create affirmations for any aspect of your life that you want to be different, or that you want to start thinking differently about. You will see affirmations resurface later in this book.

For right now, I want you to create affirmations about your eating disorder recovery, that are going to help you when you feel like giving up. Here are some examples that I came up with that you can use too, but practice coming up with your own that are individual to you as well:

1. The small steps I take each day make my recovery possible.

2. I am patient, even when obstacles or set-backs arise.

3. My eating disorder is in the past.

4. I choose to get better every day.

5. I am gentle with myself when I get stuck.

Write your affirmations down and keep them somewhere easily accessible, such as the bathroom mirror, the refrigerator, or the back of your front door!

Making the Commitment to Recovery

The most important next step you can take as we continue further along this journey together, is to make the commitment to your recovery process. I can educate you, give you advice, suggestions, and activities to complete until exhaustion. But, really, my help will be no good if you have not decided, with conviction, that you want to recover. That's why, to close this first chapter, I'll have you write a commitment statement for yourself. This will be a reminder and affirmation to get you serious about recovering.

Here is an example, but I'd encourage you to adapt it and make it your own, something that is meaningful for YOU. Keep it somewhere visible so that you can be reminded of your commitment to your recovery.

"I am committed to my recovery and achieving the highest quality of life. Nothing will get in my way. I cannot be stopped, and I deserve the very best."

I always feel SO alive after writing out my strong commitment statement. Are you feeling powerful yet? In the next chapter, I'm going to expand on this commitment aspect by helping you clarify exactly why recovery is important for you, and what it will mean for your life moving forward.

Pillar II:

Your Life's Vision

Chapter 3

You Need a Vision

"Where do you see yourself in the next 5 years?"

It's a question commonly asked in job interviews, one that can bring on the nervous jitters if you're put on the spot and haven't given it much thought.

Some people don't have a precisely laid out vision for their lives and are happy to go with the flow, and that's okay. As you now know, trying to over-control your life, or aspects of it, can be destructive.

According to research, though, people who set ambitions for themselves tend to be happier in the long-run.[15] In fact, when these ambitions provide them with

---

[15] See Rubin (2011) for more information about finding happiness through goal setting.

meaning, a sense of purpose, and direct goal-driven behavior, they are associated with better overall health as people age.[16] So, if you want to live a happy, healthy life, then constructing a meaningful vision seems like an excellent starting point, right?

Eating disorders do not make this easy, though, and I can guess that if I had to ask you right now whether you have a vision for your life, you would struggle to give me an answer.

If you do have a vision for your life, it has probably taken a back-seat because of your eating disorder. That's because eating disorders need to be front and center in your life. They consume your hopes, dreams and visions until they dwindle down to almost nothing. Their vision is simple: keep trying to control weight, shape, body size, and eating habits. Keep trying to be good enough, to be accepted, to be loveable, to be worthy, to be perfect.

This is all an illusion, of course, because in reality there is no such thing as perfection. As long as your eating disorder continues to rule your life and mind, you will never

---

[16] See Mejia (2017) for more information about purpose in life and longevity.

feel 'good enough.' It won't matter how much weight you lose, or who notices, your mindset and your core beliefs will remain the same.

How would your life be different if you believed that you were already worthy? What would you be feeling if you knew that your hopes, dreams and visions mattered, and were actually attainable?

Though it may be hard to believe, each and every person, YOU included, is a person of high value, and high worth, with a unique life purpose. Sadly, eating disorders prevent people from seeing and believing that. When you don't believe in yourself, it's difficult to believe in, construct, and follow a vision for the future. You don't think it's possible that you deserve good things, or that you're capable of having what you want. Or maybe, your identity has become so entangled in your eating disorder, that you don't even know what you want. After my own journey into recovery, knowing this always makes me so sad!

The reason that having a vision is so important for eating disorder recovery, is that it does three things:

1) It motivates and inspires you by providing you with some bigger picture goals that are meaningful to you, and

that challenge your current reality. You begin to see how your eating disorder has been holding you back.

2) It provides you with direction - when you clarify your vision, you can break it down into achievable 'chunks', working up to the ultimate end-goal. Choosing a different path (i.e. choosing life, versus your eating disorder) starts to seem more within your reach.

3) It inspires you to take action - by knowing what you need to do to attain your life's vision, you can start to take action towards that. You become aware of how you need to behave differently if you want to live a more meaningful life.

This chapter is all about helping you wade through the lies that your eating disorder has been feeding you, and to reveal and rediscover what is important to you, and what will bring you joy and happiness in your future.

How to Create Your Life's Vision

If I had a magic wand and you could make everything in your life better right now, what would your life look like, and how would you feel?

This is what you want to think about when you picture your life's vision! It is the 'ideal' life that you want for yourself, but it also goes further than that and asks, what does it FEEL like to live that life? It's important to be specific and to let your imagination run free, letting go of any limitations that you think (right now) will hold you back.

Think about it for a moment, what would you be doing with your life right now if, for example, your eating disorder, financial constraints, your limiting beliefs, and others' expectations were not a problem? How easy or difficult is it to imagine that?

I already spoke about how an eating disorder can rob you of your vision, but sometimes even coming up with a vision can be difficult because, if you're like me, you've never really thought about it much.

In the past, I struggled with my identity, knowing my true values and what I really wanted for my life. I was so used to my parents telling me what I should want and what I should do. In hindsight, it would have been incredibly helpful to have had open conversations about values as a teenager, and about how I wanted my life to look.

If you allow your parents, family, friends, or a partner to make your choices all your life, you will never figure out what's important to you. At the end of the day, you are the one who has to live with all that comes along with those choices.

However, suddenly making your own decisions when you have always relied on or expected others to choose for you, is difficult. Why? Because it means that you, alone, are accountable for those decisions and the outcomes. While that may bring up some anxiety because of the uncertainty and desire to be in control, living the other way, that is, living to please others, comes with a whole other level of disappointment. Sooner or later, you realize that you simply cannot please everyone all the time. It may feel comfortable letting others dictate your life, but again, this comfort is an illusion, and you will never find real fulfillment this way.

Now, you can see the importance of developing independence in decision-making, how impactful it is to get in touch with your hopes and dreams in life. At this point, I'm hoping you're starting to feel excited about creating a unique vision for your life!

Before we get started on how to do that, I want to demonstrate the true value that having a vision and dream for my life offered me during my own recovery journey.

By the time I reached my mid-20s, I was already on the verge of burnout: I was working at my nursing job and feeling exhausted and generally unhappy. This was made even worse by my binge-eating and purging behaviors, which had already been going on for 10 years at this point.

But one wonderful day, something happened that made me feel a way that was peculiarly unfamiliar, something that I had not felt in a really long time...Excitement, passion, drive. I learned about a business venture, and I felt an unstoppable urge to get involved. However, with all of the excitement and passion came fear. My eating disorder came up as one of the problems that would stand in my way to becoming a successful entrepreneur. But it was not the time to hold back. My vision, which was so important to me, pushed me to try recovery on my own, just one more time! So, taking matters into my own hands, and using a powerful combination of prayer, self-help books, and taking small, but consistent steps, I was finally able to create the healthy mind and body that I needed to fully recover. My vision played a huge role in propelling my recovery forward.

Creating your Vision

I'm going to take you through a series of activities that are going to be helpful in getting you to think deeply about your life: where you are now, and where you'd like to be.

Exercise 1

1. First, I want you to think about what your eating disorder has taken AWAY from you. Try to list as many things as you can, here is an example:

   My eating disorder has taken away..

   a. *my social life*

   b. *my confidence in my talents and abilities*

   c. *my precious mental energy*

d. *my joy*

e. *my desire to engage in hobbies that I used to enjoy*

2. Next, I want you to think about what your eating disorder has 'given' you. Try, again, to list as many things as possible, here is an example:

a. *My eating disorder has given me a distraction.*

b. *My eating disorder has given me comfort.*

3. Now, I want you to think about the 'costs' of what your eating disorder has given you, as they relate to your future. For example, your eating disorder may provide a distraction, but that means that you haven't had time to focus on yourself, and on doing the things that bring you true joy.

4. Next, I want you to think about how your life would be different if your eating disorder wasn't taking away the

things that you listed in the first question of the exercise.
For example:

a. *I would spend more time doing fun things with my friends, I would have the energy and confidence to go out and meet new, and interesting people who could add to my life.*

b. *I would feel more self-confident, and I would feel more open to taking risks.*

c. *I would feel more energetic and optimistic about life in general.*

d. *I would feel hopeful about the future.*

e. *I would spend more time doing the things I love.*

The point of this exercise is to get you thinking about how your eating disorder is impacting your life, as well as to build motivation for recovery by getting you to envision how things could be different.

The wonderful news is that you don't have to 'wait' to be recovered before you start constructing, or even believing in your vision. You can start right now!

It's okay if your motivation and belief is not where you think it needs to be: it's about doing the steps, and taking it from there.

Exercise 2.

Now that we've got your thinking cap warmed up, and you're starting to picture how your life might be different, I want to challenge you to get even MORE specific about what you want for your life.

What I am going to have you do, is write out your 'perfect day' in as much detail as possible. Try to engage your senses too, to make the visualization of your perfect day as realistic as possible. Think about sight, smell, vision, taste, and touch.

There is no 'wrong' or 'right' way to describe your perfect day because it is unique to you. The only 'rule' is to be as imaginative as possible, and to not limit yourself.

The following list of questions will help guide you in describing your perfect day:

1) What time do you get up in the morning?

2) How do you FEEL when you wake up, is anyone there with you?

3) Where do you live, what can you see, smell, taste, touch, around you as you wake up?

4) Do you have a morning routine?

5) How do you spend your day, what kinds of tasks or activities do you do, who do you do them with?

6) How many hours a day do you spend working/ volunteering/ studying/ doing hobbies?

7) What do you love about your day, what do you feel grateful for?

8) Do you have an evening routine?

9) When do you go to sleep, how do you feel at the end of the day?

The aim of this activity is to help figure out what gives you a sense of meaning and purpose in your life, providing insight into your core values.

This is what we are going to explore next: your values. While we have focused so far on 'what' you want for your life, your values tell us 'why' you want those things.

The Importance of Values & How to Discover Yours

Okay, so you have started discovering *what* is important to you in your life: it could be having more energy to spend on your hobbies, or perhaps waking up at 10am and working part-time from home.

What hasn't really been covered yet, is WHY these things are important to you. And that WHY is represented by your values. You may be wondering why the WHY is important at all...if you already know what's important to you, why the need to know anything more?

Well, do you remember the discussion from earlier, the one on the difficulty of making your own decisions? When you have well-defined values, when you know what matters to you and why, it's easier to make decisions! That's because you know instantly, and with conviction, whether something sits well with you and aligns with your values, or not.

Your values go further than knowing your likes and dislikes, passions, and interests: they tell a story about who you are at your very core. They provide meaning and motivate you to pursue your 'WHAT,' even when you face difficulties and obstacles along the way.

Take the example of the person who wants to wake up at 10am and work part-time from home. Let's say she is a woman in her 30's. Being able to do this is important to her because she wants to have enough quality time to spend with her children during the week. She values family and flexibility. These values push her out of her comfort zone, and inspire her to start her own business, even though it's challenging while already working a full-time job.

This is another great example of why it's important to be aware of your values. Knowing what you value will keep you fired up, even when things get tough!

Being intentional about choosing and defining your values will help you develop a stronger sense of self, and greater security within yourself. When your 'why' is missing, or if you are out of touch with your true values, you can start to feel lost and hopeless. It can lead to feelings of anxiety, emptiness, and a sense of being unfulfilled.[17] This is a dangerous place to be as far as eating disorders are concerned, if you remember the section of the book about mental health risk factors. When uncomfortable feelings are put aside, or are not processed in a healthy way, they can potentially open a void. An eating disorder can latch onto this, providing immediate relief, and blocking out any consideration for the long-term consequences. What's most insidious about the whole concept is that if you are not aware of the importance this plays in your life, you can coast through life deeply unhappy and separated from who you are at your core.

Now that you have understood a bit more about what values are, and why they are important, let's look at how you can begin to figure out what *yours* are, or which ones you'd like to start making your own.

---

[17] See Warley for more information about how finding your 'why' helps you get 'unstuck.'

Activity 3: Discovering your Core Values.

Now, take a look at the table of typical values on the next page. I want you to choose the top 10 values that resonate most with you. You may notice that there is some overlap between some of them.

Try not to think too much about this activity, go with your 'gut' feeling and choose the values that just feel right to you. You can start with more than 10, then reduce them until you are left with 10.

Achievement	Adventure	Ambition	Authenticity	Autonomy
Balance	Beauty	Boldness	Bravery	Calmness
Community	Competency	Creativity	Curiosity	Challenge
Change	Consistency	Competitiveness	Control	Cooperation
Compassion	Commitment	Charity	Contentment	Courage
Determination	Discipline	Diversity	Dependability	Drive
Excitement	Ethics	Expressive	Equality	Endurance
Expertise	Family	Fairness	Fame	Financial freedom
Fun	Faith	Forgiveness	Fitness	Flexibility
Friendship	Growth	Generous	Goodness	Helpful
Honesty	Humility	Health	Humor	Hope
Independence	Integrity	Initiative	Influence	Intimacy
Joy	Justice	Kindness	Knowledge	Leadership
Learning	Love	Loyalty	Moderation	Mastery
Peace	Popularity	Patience	Spirituality	Security
Safety	Serenity	Self-sufficient	Satisfied	Tradition
Truth	Time	Vitality	Wealth	Wisdom

Table 2

Now that you have found your 'top 10' core values, let's see if you can get them down to just 5!

Exercise 3 - Self-Reflection

Now that you have discovered the top 5 values that you feel resonate most with you, I want you take some time to think about the following:

1) In what ways are you already living in line with your core values?

For example, if one of my top values was family, maybe I am already living in line with that value by making sure that I spend quality time with my family everyday.

2) In what ways are your decisions, actions, and current lifestyle in conflict with your core values?

For example, if one of my core values is faith, perhaps I have been completely neglecting my spiritual side by not spending time in prayer or meditation in the mornings like I used to.

3) How would living in alignment with your core values change your life? For example, if one of my core values was ambition, and my ambition was to start a business, if I was living in alignment with this core value, then I would be on my way to starting a business. Whereas

right now, my eating disorder and the related symptoms (like lack of energy, and lack of self-confidence), may be preventing me from living in alignment with this core value.

The purpose of these two activities is to help you discover what makes your life meaningful, and how your life might look if you used your values to guide your decisions and actions in life.

Putting It all Together

At this point, I'm picturing that it's starting to get a little easier to imagine a life that is different to the one you're living right now: one where you feel happy, fulfilled, and excited about your future!

Exercise 4 - Dream Away!

I want to challenge you to take what you've learned about your 'WHAT' and your 'WHY,' and write down some dreams or goals that you have for your life. Try to come up with at least 8 - 10. Again, it doesn't matter what they are, as long as they are:

1) true to who you are

2) excite and challenge you

3) give you hope for the future.

Here are some examples: I'd like to...

1. Travel the world.

2. To be a parent.

3. To have my own online store.

4. Find a more fulfilling job or line of work.

5. Heal from my eating disorder permanently.

6. To live in a different state or country.

7. To do missionary work in areas of poverty.

8. Change majors and study something new for my dream career.

Now, of the 8-10 that you wrote down, choose your top 3!

Exercise 4, Part 2: Self-reflection

Now that you have had some time to think about some of your dreams for your life, I want you to ask yourself the following questions:

1. Why do you want this dream?

2. How would reaching this dream make you feel?

3. What has been holding you back from reaching for this dream?

The purpose of these activities is to get you excited and connected with the dreams that you may have forgotten, or even dreams that you may have thought about for the first time while going through this chapter!

This is also going to help you in the next exercise, which is the final part of this chapter.

Exercise 5. Creating a 'Vision Board'

Finally, it's time to pull everything that you've learned about yourself from this chapter together. I'm inviting you to create a 'vision board'.

We have just been through what is important to you. You can think of a 'vision board' as a creative work that uses imagery to represent everything that you want for your life. As it is a unique representation of your deepest hopes, dreams, and wishes for your future, you have full artistic license to create your vision board in any way that feels right for you!

Visualization is a common and effective tool that has been used successfully by professional athletes for a long time! Studies have shown that athletes who visualized their performance in great detail, were able to improve their live performance, as well as their confidence[18] Visualizing doesn't just work for athletes though, it can work for anyone! You can think of visualization as preparing your brain for what to expect. In doing so, you automatically start to do things and to act in accordance with what you want to unfold.

I'll share my own experience on how I created my own vision board in order to inspire you with some ideas for creating yours.

---

[18] See Pillay (2011) for more information about the science of visualization.

As a first step to creating my vision board, I bought a large, firm piece of posterboard. Then, since I had a bunch of old magazines lying around the house, I took some time to go through them and I cut out all of the images and words that stood out to me, that resonated with my vision for my life. Finally, when I had cut out enough images, words and symbols to fill the posterboard, I arranged them and stuck them on the card, in a kind of collage. My vision board is full of people on outdoor adventures, serene nature photos, family, and a few statements I've written out by hand that remind me of who I am.

I put my vision board on the wall in my bedroom where I can see it everyday to remind myself of my WHAT and my WHY. Seeing your vision board daily can help provide you with comfort, hope, and remind you to persevere, even when you may be having an 'off-day.' Do you remember the phrase "out of sight, out of mind"? You'll always find that the opposite is also true, and powerful!

You may be wondering, now that you are clear on your life's vision, how do you actually go about making it your new reality?

Maybe at this moment, it feels like a very distant dream. Perhaps thinking about what it will take to get there feels daunting, even defeating. That's because, right now, there is probably a large disparity between where you are now and where you'd like to be. That's okay. Rome wasn't built in a day. And that's why, in the next chapter, you are going to learn exactly how you can take small, manageable steps to get closer and closer to your ultimate vision for your life. You will discover that fulfilling your dreams is *absolutely* in the realm of possibility.

Pillar III:

Building Habits for the Life of Your Dreams

Chapter 4

How Habits & Routine Shape Your Life and Affect Eating Disorder Recovery

It's easy to look at somebody else's life and think,

"WOW. How did that person get *so. darn. Lucky?*"

As social creatures, we have an innate tendency to compare ourselves to others, and this has become even more prominent with the dawn of social media. Social comparison can function to either support a positive or negative view of ourselves. If you often compare yourself to others who you perceive as 'better' in some way, this is known as upward social comparison.[19] This upward social comparison can lead to one of two outcomes:

---

[19] See Nortje (2021) for more information about Social Comparison Theory.

Let's say you started comparing yourself to somebody who appears to have their career together, and you don't have a clue about where you are headed. You may either 1.) end up feeling much worse about yourself, and beat yourself up about it; or 2.) It can inspire you to improve yourself, so that you draw closer to having the things you want for yourself that you see others already have.

The danger of comparing yourself to others who you see on social media channels, like Instagram and Facebook these days, is that it is very difficult to tell what is real from what is fake. Peoples' intentions when it comes to social media, generally, are to portray themselves in the best light possible.

Think about the last time that you noticed somebody had shared their vulnerabilities, in plain sight, on a public platform? It doesn't happen often.

Since it is so easy to mask your true self online, you don't actually see the struggle and the challenges that people have gone through to get the 'result' that appears on social media. It is also impossible to tell whether the images and videos you are being bombarded with on a daily basis are an accurate representation of peoples' realities.

That woman that you follow on social media? The one with the 100k followers and her own clothing brand? What you don't see is the blood, sweat, and tears that she poured into creating her own business from scratch. You don't see the sleepless nights, or how she almost gave up...And that woman you follow with 10k followers, who presents herself as a travel blogger? You don't see the sacrifice, and years of work she put into building up her reputation to the point where she could make her digital nomad lifestyle a reality.

Instead, what you do see is a version of these peoples' reality, as it exists right now, or rather how they want you to believe it exists (confusing, I know!).

When all you see is a shiny, faultless end-result in neat little squares, your brain uses mental short-cuts to process this, like "that's unfair, she's just lucky." When you attribute others' success to things like luck, in psychology, this is called 'attribution error.' [20] That is, we are prone to making errors when evaluating others' good fortune.

---

[20] See Roberts (2018) as cited in Abnormal Returns for more on attribution error.

I can guarantee, though, that anybody who has had a vision, or a goal, that was important to them, that they desperately wanted to and DID eventually achieve, did not do so overnight. They had processes in place that gave them direction and helped guide them on how to get there.

Researchers that have studied what makes people successful and able to create the lives they want for themselves, found that a personality trait called 'grit' and 'perseverance' could be responsible. [21] Grit has been associated with determination and passion over the long-term. Angela Duckworth (2021), who has researched 'grit' extensively, believes that it can be taught.

Actually, in this book, I have already started teaching you two different ways to develop this trait, and in this chapter, I will introduce a third way. So far, you have started learning about what it means to have grit by:

1. Focusing on developing a recovery mindset, which was covered in chapter two. An important part to perseverance is having the attitude to keep going, to

---

[21] See Duckworth (2021) for more information on the trait 'grit.'

never give up, even when you feel overcome by your circumstances, or feel that you have failed.

2. Exploring and solidifying your life's vision: another crucial part to having grit is having passion. Passion will reignite the spark and keep you working towards your vision.

Now, we are going to delve further into the third way through cultivating habits, which will help with the persistence factor over the long-term.

Remember we spoke about how, right now, your life vision may seem like nothing more than a distant dream? Well, you're about to find how developing small habits is going to transform that mindset completely and bring your vision closer.

What are Habits?

Habits can be defined as "rituals and behaviors that we perform automatically."[22] Many of our habits, because they have been practiced multiple times (think about brushing your teeth, and washing your hands after using the

---

[22] See Soots (2015) for more information on what habits are.

restroom), become an effortless part of our everyday lives. Good habits, like these, function positively in our lives. Unfortunately, bad habits can develop and become just as automatic as good habits. Bad habits are dysfunctional and cause us harm in some way. Think about smoking: it may help relieve tension and stress in the moment, but at the expense of long-term health.

You can think of eating disorders and the patterns they create as 'bad habits' that have become automatic, too. Take binge-eating and purging, for example. The act of binge-eating is a habit that, as you discovered in chapter one, may have developed to manage uncomfortable emotions and intense psychological pain. This habit, although 'helpful' at treating the pain at the time, is harmful in the long-term. Not only can it lead to excessive weight gain, and lowered self-esteem, it also increases the risk for adopting a secondary habit, like purging. This comes with more complications, as you've also learned in chapter one.

Restrictive eating also causes bad habits to become ingrained in much the same way. When you restrict food and you lose weight, the weight loss acts as positive reinforcement to keep restricting, and to keep losing more weight. This acts as to boost self-esteem initially but in the long-term, your self-esteem suffers because you never feel 'thin enough,' and you never feel truly satisfied. Also, if you gain a bit of weight, or your weight loss starts to slow down, your self-esteem can take a knock. You feel that you've failed, and that you need to try harder, and so the cycle goes.

Although your eating disorder behaviors may have been a conscious choice initially, with time, they may become built-in and may also be repeated on a subconscious level, just like habits. Eventually, I began to feel that my habit of choosing my eating disorders behaviors had become an addiction. I became so dependent on them in order to feel good and in control that it resembled how a drug addict behaves. Seeing my pattern as an addiction helped me to take serious action, which allowed me to find healing. At the end of the day, I didn't want to feel like I was being controlled by something. I desired to grow to a place where I made better decisions, and was in control of my own behavior. Eventually, I came to believe that I could decide to take the power into my own hands and break this addiction to using food and the controlling behaviors around it as a coping mechanism.

The reason that habits are so hard to break is largely due to this 'subconscious' element. Habits can be so sneaky.

The trick when trying to break bad habits, is not to focus so much on 'stopping' or 'quitting' some behavior. Take, for instance, what happens when I tell you not to think of purple teddy bears. I bet that you imagined 100's of purple teddy bears, right? A similar thing happens when you try to focus purely on 'stopping' or 'quitting' something. You can start to obsess about it more.

What you can try to do instead of just 'stopping' bad habits, is to develop NEW habits. It takes on average, 2 months for a new habit to become automatic[23] and the more new habits you incorporate into your life, the less room there will be for the unhelpful ones! This is exactly what happened in my case.

When recovering from my eating disorder, I started to introduce a healthful habit into my daily life. I chose habits that I felt the recovered version of me would do each and every day.

The goals were very small - no-brainer small - because at the time, my eating disorder had such a massive impact on my physical and mental state. I was constantly

---

[23] See Clear (n.d.) for more information on developing habits.

depleted, completely lacking in motivation, and I didn't feel like doing anything at all. I had to start so small that I almost questioned whether my actions would make a difference.

This is where I want you to shoot for in the beginning. Make your habits so easy that it would be kind of silly not to do them. Try, for example, taking the stairs to the fourth floor at your job every day. Don't use the elevator unless you are carrying things that need to be delivered without dropping them! If you need to increase your water intake, bring a large water bottle with you to work and refill it each time you get halfway through it, and set a goal of how much you want to drink each day.

This method of adding habits is what worked for me. When I got one habit solidified into my day to day life, I would add another one. After 6 weeks of doing this, I was snowballing myself into recovery, one healthful practice at a time, and I no longer had room for binge-eating habits! I had slowly and mindfully 'crowded out' the habits that were keeping me sick and stuck in the same place, and there was no longer room for them with the new ones I was practicing.

The key to creating habits that 'stick,' is to incorporate them slowly, mastering one habit at a time, before adding more. If you try to implement too many changes at once, you will become overwhelmed. Doing too much at once is unsustainable, and unenjoyable, I might add. You also want to be looking at introducing habits with your long-term future in mind. Small habits are going to compound and give your lifestyle a makeover, which permanently supports your lifelong wellbeing if you keep it up.

Now, let's consider why creating small daily habits is going to be crucial to your recovery journey.

Why Create Habits?

Setting habits that are inherently good provides you with multiple pathways that you can move through to attain your goals. These pathways offer clear progression on how you can go from living a life where you feel stuck, to one that you love and are excited to live!

It is important in eating disorder recovery, to follow-through intentions with habits. Without planned action (habits), intentions are just that: intentions.

If you have intentions without habits, you risk moving forward in a disorganized fashion and repeatedly restarting. This was me during the beginning years of my recovery. I lacked the mindset I needed to truly step into recovery. I was WAITING to feel better. I thought "I'll go to therapy, it will help," "I'll listen to podcasts and that will help." They helped a little, but not enough to make the impact of leaving behind my eating disordered behaviors and to start working on healing my relationship with myself, food and my body.

In the throes of your eating disorder recovery, because you have to relinquish control of your existing habits around food, and your body, there will be many times where you feel out of control. It is in these moments, that you will be most vulnerable to relapse.

Developing upgraded, replacement habits, however, can help keep you grounded. That's because, when you've identified the habits that you want to adopt, you commit to doing them despite how you feel or what is going through your mind. It is clear in advance what needs to be done, and you just 'do it.' That is what habits are about: they are about just doing something without having to think about it. It's like you're doing a behavior automatically, and that takes very little effort. Although routine and habits may seem unnatural and may not feel fun at first, with enough repetition, they become second-nature. In time, what once feels unnatural and difficult can become an integrated part of your life.

I want to reassure you that while you may not see it right now, when you are connecting with the recovered, healthy you, when you are engaging in habits that are of the new you and not of your old self, you begin to connect more with what healing feels like. It becomes something that you want more and more of. You no longer desire to keep seeking comfort from your dysfunctional habits because you are aware that they have been keeping you stuck. At this point, it becomes easier to include more habits and building blocks that get you oriented in the direction of healing.

The amazing thing that happens when you start implementing habits and 'mastering' those habits, is that it builds up more motivation and enhances your self-esteem. When you reach your smaller goals, you get the confidence to tackle bigger ones because you know that you are capable and you have experienced the benefits that the previous habit brought to your life.

How to Create Habits

The habits that you want to adopt in your daily life can be thought of in the same way as goals. They are something that will require time and consistent effort to achieve.

Since habits are like goals, you can use a common goal-setting strategy applied to creating habits. The strategy that I'm going to teach you is easy to remember because it uses the acronym S.M.A.R.T.

The SMART goals strategy was first developed in 1981 by George Doral.[24] It has since been widely and successfully used as a self-help tool to guide people like you and I to create, monitor and achieve what we set out to do.

SMART stands for specific, measurable, achievable, relevant, and time-limited.[24] I'm going to explain each of these in more detail, using the following example of a habit I'd like to adopt. Let's say it is, "I want to be more healthy."

---

[24] See Doral (1981) for more information on the SMART goals strategy.

S for specific

If we look at this goal as it is, it is quite vague. How do you plan to be more healthy? It doesn't really tell us what is meant by the desire, or what action is needed to get there. When setting goals, we need to be specific. That way, we are not left confused about how to reach our goal, or what our goal even is, or means to us.

So, let's try that again...

"I will drink 2 liters of water every day."

Can you see here, how I have taken my initial goal of "I want to be healthier" a step further?

You can do the same by thinking of what would be the first, small thing that you could see yourself doing if you wanted to be "healthier."

Also, in making my goal specific, I have focused on simplifying my health goal, and picking just one thing to focus on. This will help me stay focused on what I need to do, drink 2 liters of water (not 1, or 3 liters), every day (not every second day, or once a week). Notice also how I have stated my habit/goal in the positive. It is always better to do it this way because when stating a goal in the negative, for example, "I don't want to restrict my food," it is harder to take action on that. A better way to phrase that would be, "I will eat at least 3 wholesome meals a day and 2 small snacks that make me feel satisfied." This example demonstrates unfearful, forward-thinking, and projects your mind and actions in the direction of your goal instead of keeping you focused on what you *don't* want.

M is for measurable

Your habit/goal should be something that you can track and measure. If you're able to quantify your goal, this makes it much easier to determine whether you are making the progress you want to see.

In the adjusted example, "I will drink 2 liters of water every day," how might you track this? One way could be to mark each day on your calendar that you achieved this goal with an 'X.' You could also keep track of your daily water intake using a notebook, where each day you write down how much water you drank that day. Some days, you may surprise yourself and exceed your target!

A is for achievable

Your goal should be something that is challenging but still realistic, and therefore achievable.

Using the same water example, for many people, remembering to drink enough water can be difficult. What might make it easier and achievable, though, would be to keep a large water bottle at your desk, or to take a water bottle around with you at all times. You could even set an alarm on your phone at 2-3 hour intervals to remind yourself to keep drinking water. Although remembering to drink a lot of water each day is difficult, you can see how it is still achievable.

R is for relevant

When thinking about the goal you're going to set, you want to make sure that it is important to you, that it lines up with the values you determined in chapter 3. You want to ask yourself, does this goal serve me?

For example, if you suffer from chronic headaches due to dehydration, then drinking water might be a great first goal to set. It's not too intimidating, and it's relevant to building motivation for recovery, and feeling better physically.

T is for time-limited

You should set a timeline for when you estimate to have integrated your habit into your daily life for having reached your goal.

As we found out earlier, habits, on average take 8 weeks to become automatic. So when setting a habit, 8 weeks would be a good benchmark. When it comes to goal setting, especially when you want to set bigger goals, this, of course, would need to be adjusted accordingly! Remember, the timeline needs to be realistic too, and if you have been dealing with some of your unhelpful eating disorder habits for a long time, then trying out alternative, health-minded habits and making them permanent, may take much longer than just 8 weeks.

I want to tell you that it doesn't matter how long it takes you to incorporate and master small habits. What does matter is that you don't give up. In my own journey, setting habits felt really unnatural at first. I must have started over hundreds of times! The thing is, when I was stuck with my eating disorder mindset, I felt that I didn't have what it took to live a life filled with healthy habits. This kind of thinking made me want to give up and often left me feeling defeated, not wanting to even try at all. But that is a normal part of the process.

What I realized later, is that I just hadn't connected with the desire to have that level of change or discipline yet: it was only once I tried, tried again, and successfully started incorporating healthy habits into my life that I saw the benefits, and my mindset changed. It took a lot of hard work and discipline, and going against what felt comforting and familiar. If I don't reiterate this part, that creating habits takes a lot of discipline and sacrifice, then I won't be holding up my commitment to guide you into healing. If I'm being real, it's going to be a challenge. But the worth-it things in life are often challenging. They require you to step out of your comfort zone. That's why I encourage you to take little steps and to take it slow with habit-building. If you feel like you've failed, dust yourself off and try again. You are worth it and you deserve to have a life where you're thriving!

Now that you have understood how to create habits and set goals, think about 3 habits that you'd like to set for yourself starting right now!

Activity 5.

Think about 3 habits that would make a positive difference in your life, and to your recovery. Then, applying what we've learned in this chapter so far, and the SMART strategy, use the template on the next page to make your habits SMART. You can also use a notebook if you prefer.

You can find a SMART goals worksheet to help you structure your habits in my E-guide, "7 Life-Changing Hacks for Learning How to Eat Without Fear of Weight Gain" as a bonus gift to you for purchasing this book. I don't want you missing out on this! You can get your digital copy at 'bonusguide.vitalitycoaching.org'

What is the habit you'd like to implement?

_____

_____

S - specific (what do I want to achieve?)

M - measurable (how will I measure my progress?)

A - achievable (how will I make this realistic?)

R - relevant (why is this important to me?)

T - time-limited (when do I want to have achieved this goal?)

Now rewrite the initial habit you wrote with the SMART principles in mind:

_____

_____

Pillar IV:

Engaging your Support System

Chapter 5

Getting the Support You Need to Recover

Eating disorders, as you learned in chapter one, like to keep you isolated from your loved ones and from your communities. That is how they exert control over your life, by keeping you locked in cycles of pain and shame, and having you believe that only they can provide the solution that you need. They are masters of deceit and will tell you every lie in the book to keep you dependent on the scraps of comfort that they provide.

What you can be sure of, though, when it comes to the prevention of eating disorders, is that social support is critical. That means that a huge part of recovery from an eating disorder depends on building up a strong social support system.

Think about us human beings as a species: we are born completely helpless. If we do not have a responsible adult tending to our basic needs for food and shelter from day one, we will not survive. Equally, or even more important for healthy development, is building a bond with our primary caregivers that makes us feel loved and comforted.

The need to develop close, emotional bonds, or attachment, was confirmed in studies conducted in the 50's, 60's, and 70's on infant Rhesus monkeys.[25] The long-term impact that the studies had on some of the monkeys was devastating, but the experiments did teach us a lot about attachment and its significance for healthy social and emotional development.

It all started with American psychologist Harlow,[26] who wanted to prove that attachment was not formed only because caregivers provided their offspring with food. So, Harlow took infant monkeys and isolated them from their mothers, giving them two surrogate mothers instead. One

---

[25] See Harlow's studies (1965, 1958, and 1971) for more information on attachment theory.

[26] See Harlow (1958) for more information on how attachment is developed.

mother was made out of wire and provided food, and another was made out of soft cloth, and provided no food. What Harlow found was that the infant monkeys preferred to spend time with the soft cloth mothers, and turned to these mothers for comfort when confronted with fearful stimuli. This proved that attachment is about more than food: it is about physical affection and the comfort this provides.[25]

This is where the cruelty of Harlow's experiments is exposed: in those monkeys that Harlow kept isolated for more than 90 days, they struggled to overcome the trauma caused by being reared without a real mother. For those that were kept isolated for up to a year, some of them never got past it. When they were finally reintroduced to other monkeys, the monkeys that were isolated for more than 90 days presented with fear and didn't know how to socialize. They were picked on by the other monkeys, and they had issues with mating. Many of the female monkeys were incapable as mothers later on.[27]

Since humans share 93% DNA with the Rhesus monkeys that were used in the experiments, the findings are

---

[27] See Harlow & Suomi (1971) for more information on the impact of social isolation on attachment.

comparable.[28] These, and later studies, show time and time again that early relationships and the ability to develop close bonds with caregivers is essential for healthy social and emotional development in later life.[25]

Taking the gravity of these findings into consideration, you are going to learn in this chapter how you can draw on your available social resources to help boost your recovery process. You will look at how to engage professional and community services, as well as your loved ones during the recovery process.

Professional Services - Therapy

Eating disorders are diagnosable mental illnesses. What this means is that there is enough evidence and research out there to acknowledge that they exist, and that they cause many people a lot of pain and suffering. It also means that treatment has been successfully trialled and recommended for use for eating disorders by licensed professionals. These licensed professionals, or

---

[28] See National Institutes of Health (2007) for more information on the genetic similarity between Rhesus monkeys and humans.

psychologists, are trained in, and use evidence-based methods to help cure eating disorders.

The Benefits of Working with a Psychologist

Besides psychologists being very knowledgeable and well-trained, there is something innately different about speaking with a psychologist, than speaking, for example, with a family member or friend. You have probably noticed that when telling a friend or family member about your problems, their first response is to try and offer a solution. A psychologist won't do this, at least not off the bat. Instead, they'll intently listen to what you have to say, offer support and understanding, and help you better process and reflect on what it is you're experiencing.

Perhaps you have also noticed, when talking to friends and family, that they often offer you advice that they feel would be best for you. Their advice is based on their own opinions and biases. A psychologist is trained to take a neutral stance, and to be as objective as possible. They will never judge your situation or offer you unsolicited advice. They act more as facilitators, helping you gain better insight into yourself. This doesn't mean that they will never call you out, or push you: this may be needed sometimes. However, they are trained to do this in ways that are effective and that make an impact.

Another thing that you can rest assured with, when it comes to psychologists, is that they are guided by an ethical code of conduct, which prioritizes confidentiality of their clients' private information. So, you can be confident that whatever you tell them (within certain limits), will never be shared with anyone else.

In my own experience with therapy, I've always found a benefit to going, whether it was individual therapy, eating disorder therapy, or couples therapy. For me, talking about things with a therapist that you can't express to your friends and family due to relationships and biases, and not wanting to hurt people's feelings, is helpful and cathartic!

I also want to share some of the downsides I experienced with therapy, as well as ways that you can make therapy work for you. The point is not to turn you off to therapy: I am a strong advocate for seeking professional mental health support. This is more so that you are aware of what to expect, and also about how to make therapy work for you as part of your recovery, and so that you can make informed choices.

The Downsides of Therapy

The biggest downsides for me about therapy were the costs, as well as how eating disorder treatment was approached.

I attended two separate therapy programs that were tailored to eating disorders. I ended up dropping out both times because the bills stacked up on top of each other, and I couldn't maintain my living expenses and pay for treatment at the same time. As a student working part-time, this issue was especially tough. I had to put a lot of bills on my credit card, which was difficult to pay off and resulted in a lot of debt. Even with insurance, the bills were insurmountable. Both times, I left treatment unrecovered and out of balance financially.

The other issue I had with the programs was their approach to treatment. Although the second program was a more inclusive approach to eating disorder therapy, it still only did so much for my recovery. During the years after therapy, I went on to develop my 7 pillar system and recovered once and for all! In my own experience, therapy helped up to a certain point, but what led to my full recovery was including all 7 pillars. The holistic approach to healing

I discovered leaves no stone unturned, and gives you SO much more than just recovery from an eating disorder!

Making Therapy Work for You

Therapy is a huge investment in yourself. It's a big deal to open yourself up and entrust someone with your vulnerabilities. Having been to therapy many times myself, I'm going to share what I believe will be valuable for you to bear in mind, as you embark on your recovery journey through therapy:

1. Get a therapist that you trust and feel comfortable with. Studies have shown that the client-therapist relationship can largely impact recovery, even more so than the therapist's specific technique or approach.[29] After my recovery, I worked with a therapist that was perfect for me. She shared her own story with me about going through an eating disorder, and it helped deepen my trust in her. I was able to make breakthrough after breakthrough with her, and this particular client-therapist relationship is something I'll always be grateful for.

---

[29] See Horvath (2001) for more information on the therapeutic relationship and its impact on therapeutic outcomes.

2. Definitely discuss different treatment options with your therapist, and decide on one that you both feel will work best for you based on your goals. It is important that the therapeutic approach used resonates with your worldview. If you and your therapist have wildly different ways of viewing the world, then you will find it difficult to agree on what strategies or approach to use. Even though therapists are trained to be objective and flexible in their approach, they usually tend to stick with one or two approaches. Don't be afraid to ask your therapist questions, or to speak up if you disagree. Remember, this is about you and a therapist can always refer you to another therapist who may be a better fit for the kind of treatment or approach you are looking for.

The next part of this chapter shares helpful information on some of the more common approaches used by therapists. Use this section to get a better idea about what to expect when it comes to what you'll be learning and focusing on in therapy.

Types of Therapy

1. Cognitive Behavioral Therapy

Cognitive Behavioral Therapy is one of the first-line treatments for Binge-Eating Disorder and Anorexia Nervosa.[30] In Cognitive Behavioral Therapy, psychologists teach you how to become more aware of how your thoughts, feelings, and behaviors are interconnected. They ultimately teach that thoughts arise in response to different situations, and that these thoughts influence how you feel, which in turn, influence how you behave. Remember the activity we learned in chapter 2 (self-monitoring)? This activity was guided by the principles of Cognitive Behavioral Therapy, or 'CBT'. The purpose of CBT is to create more awareness, so that you can make a conscious effort to change your thinking patterns, adopt healthier perspectives, and try out new behaviors.[31]

---

[30] See Murphy et al. (2010) for more information on Cognitive Behavioral Therapy for Eating Disorders.

[31] See APA (2017) for more information on Cognitive Behavioral Therapy.

2. Dialectical Behavior Therapy.

Dialectical Behavior Therapy, also known as 'DBT', grew out of Cognitive Behavioral Therapy, and focuses more on teaching emotion regulation and interpersonal skills. It is also different to CBT in that it often includes a combination of individual and group sessions. CBT is provided one on one. In Dialectical Behavior Therapy, psychologists teach four main skills. These include, mindfulness (being present and aware in the moment); distress tolerance (coping with heightened emotions); interpersonal effectiveness (setting boundaries in relationships and learning effective communication); and emotion regulation (strategies for managing thoughts, emotions, and subsequent behavior).[32]

3. Eye Movement Desensitization and Reprocessing (EMDR)

EMDR is a type of therapy that is especially useful if you have experienced any trauma. It is usually used in combination with other types of therapy, since the main

---

[32] See Cowden (2020) for more information on Dialectical Behavior Therapy.

function of EMDR is to help reprocess trauma and prevent negative memories from intruding on and impacting your daily life. EMDR therapy works by focusing on bilateral stimulation, which is created by having you follow a psychologist's fingers as they move bilaterally. This has been found to provide access to the part of the brain that stores and processes memories, and that may have become stuck due to unprocessed or improperly processed trauma.

Initially, in an EMDR session, you'd be asked to recall painful memories, and how they have made you feel about yourself, as you follow the psychologist's fingers moving side to side. Once the trauma has been sufficiently processed in a safe space, and no longer causes such grave disturbance, reprocessing begins. In the reprocessing part, you are asked to focus on a new, positive self-belief as the psychologist uses the bilateral stimulation technique again.[33]

4. Acceptance and Commitment Therapy (ACT)

Acceptance and Commitment Therapy, like DBT, also has its roots in Cognitive Behavioral Therapy, however, Acceptance and Commitment Therapy does not focus on

---

[33] See EMDR Institute (n.d.) for more information on EMDR Therapy.

changing negative thoughts. Instead, it focuses on strategies like mindfulness (being present), and raises the argument that negative thoughts, as well as pain and discomfort, are an ordinary part of life, as much as positive thoughts and feelings are. With this in mind, Acceptance and Commitment Therapy tries to help you find acceptance for all of your thoughts, both good and bad. [34]

Now that you have understood the role of a psychologist in the recovery process, and have learned about the most common approaches that they may use in therapy, I'll explore with you the role of a coach in eating disorder recovery.

Psychologists versus Coaches: What is the Difference?

Psychologists and coaches differ in the way they are trained, their scope of practice, and in how they approach their clients. Psychologists are trained in the diagnosis and treatment of all mental disorders and they undergo a rigorous study and practical program that leads to state licensure. Depending on where in the world they practice, they may be

---

[34] See Eating Disorder Hope (2018) for more information on ACT.

required to have completed up to master's or PHD level education.

Coaches also study mental health, but they are not qualified to treat severe mental health disorders. There is more of a focus on managing current issues, and on paving the way forward without as much emphasis on the past. Coaches also complete extensive study programs which qualify them for registration with reputable organizations, such as The International Coaching Federation. Although they are not licensed to treat mental illnesses, they often work closely with other professionals, like psychologists to help progress in recovery from mental illness. Essentially, they help support the treatment plan of therapy with their clients day to day.[35]

As a health coach, I support my clients in reaching their health goals, with a special focus on holistic eating disorder recovery. I love working closely with women 1:1 to help them get past their stuck points and heal from their eating disorders. The most rewarding part about being a coach is guiding women on nutrition and lifestyle that is

---

35 See Costin (2020) for more information on the differences between coaching and therapy.

individualized to their own unique needs. We are not 'one size fits all', and I love breaking out of that idea with the 7-Pillar System and acknowledging the bio-individuality of people. You can book a free 1:1 coaching session with me by visiting my website at

www.vitalitycoaching.org/coaching-program/.

What if I Can't Afford Therapy or Don't Have Insurance Coverage?

It can be very disheartening if, despite being desperate for professional help and support, you find that you do not meet the criteria for insurance coverage or acceptance into a recovery program. This is sadly the reality for many people out there, but it doesn't mean you are out of options.

What it *does* mean is that you need to be smart about mobilizing your other resources. Consider hiring a coach, or utilize self-help and personal development books. Focus on books that cover topics like habit formation, exploring your dreams, and transforming your mindset. These books often draw on psychological models that we discussed earlier, such as CBT, and teach practical coping skills.

Think about this as a temporary plan, as you perhaps look for a job that has health benefits and that could allow you to be insured for some time.

Community Resources

It is easy to feel alone in your struggle with your eating disorder, so much so that you probably wouldn't think that there would be others in your local community who are going through the same, or a similar struggle!

I bet that if you did a quick search on Google, you would find at least one local, in-person support group dedicated to eating disorder recovery.

"Meet Up" is a popular app that you can use to find local, in-person support groups. "Meet Up" also advertises virtual support groups, that anyone around the world can join and gain access to. You can browse "Meet Up" by connecting to their app or website, here:

https://www.meetup.com/

Facebook, Instagram and Youtube are also rich with online communities that offer support for eating disorder recovery.

Support groups are often started by people who have struggled with and overcome similar problems that you are dealing with. You will meet others who you can relate to, and vice versa. This is invaluable as it offers a platform for others to share what has and has not worked for them, and for you to also share your own insights. This creates a sense of connection to others. With the support of a like-minded community, the load of recovery feels somewhat lightened. You feel understood, and you have space to express your emotions instead of bottling them up, which as we have learned, can fuel more eating disordered behaviors, limiting beliefs and low self-esteem.

It's vitally important that you take responsibility in getting a support system in place that you can lean on and where you can help provide support back to others. We all need to be seen, accepted, and received to make progress. Having community with people who are walking through the same challenges will give you a powerful sense of belonging that often feels missing in eating disorder recovery. Our unique support tribe provides daily tips for eating disorder recovery, and we take every opportunity to be there for each other. We show up and remind each other how loved, capable and empowered we are, and to never give up fighting for yourself and for the life in recovery you deserve. Come join us and be a part of our tribe at

www.facebook.com/groups/eatingdisorderrecoverytribe.

Family and Friends

It can feel more daunting to admit that you have an eating disorder to family and friends than to friends online that you've never met. That's because there seems to be less at stake with a person online if the conversation doesn't go as planned - this person doesn't really know you and you will never have to face them again if you don't want to.

When it comes to sharing sensitive information about your eating disorder with your loved ones, you might worry that they won't understand, or that they will start acting differently around you once they know the truth. However, all these kinds of thoughts about how others may react limit you. They stop you from trying out other coping mechanisms, like leaning on loved ones, and keep you reliant on your eating disorder to cope.

In saying this, you want to tell family members and friends who you really trust, and who you feel comfortable being honest with. Telling loved ones about your eating disorder can be helpful to your recovery in a few different ways:

1. When you tell someone you love about the problems you are facing, it lightens the burden that you feel. It also becomes easier to open up in the future, and you learn that there are other ways to cope with your emotions. You learn that being open and connecting with people can provide the same comfort that you get from your eating disorder.

2. It can make you feel less alone and more supported. You can share information with your loved ones about eating disorders so that they get a better idea of what you are going through and know how to be there for you.

3. You can share information with your loved ones about your triggers, so that they can be more cautious and sensitive when it comes to making comments about your eating, weight, and food.

4. While support groups, psychologists, coaches, and online communities are extremely helpful, being vulnerable with the people you really care about can offer an even deeper sense of connection and freedom. Your loved ones are also probably your most accessible

social resource, so learning to trust and lean on them to help you cope in difficult situations is paramount for sustained recovery and relapse prevention.

As we close this chapter, take action on 2-3 of the following to activate this part of the recovery process:

1. Open up to one person you love and trust about your eating disorder.

2. Join an online or in-person eating disorder support group in your local area.

3. Make a list of 2-3 books you'd like to purchase next to help in this area.

4. Book a free coaching session at

   www.vitalitycoaching.org/coaching-program/.

5. Find an eating disorder treatment program or therapist and call for information. Take it one step further and set up an intake appointment.

Pillar V:

Spirituality and Forging Your Identity

Chapter 6

How God and Spirituality Can Help Your Recovery

If you're thinking about skipping over this chapter because you do not believe in any religion or a higher power...please don't! There is more to spirituality than belief in God, a Higher Power, or religion. If you don't believe in God, you can still embrace your spiritual side.

By the end of this chapter, you will understand the difference between religion and spirituality. You will know what steps you can start taking right away to start building your spiritual life, and you will recognize the benefits that these can bring for your recovery, and for your future.

Spirituality Versus Religion

The key takeaway when it comes to spirituality versus religion, is that you can be spiritual without having to commit to a specific religion. Spirituality and religion are not one in the same: spirituality often holds unique meaning to different people, since what it means to be spiritual can be interpreted in various ways.

While religion is based on fixed beliefs and practices that are shared by all who follow that religion, spirituality is much more all-encompassing and individual. Spirituality is more about making your own meaning and developing your own beliefs that guide you in life and that bring you a sense of inner fulfillment.[36] So you don't need to be religious, or believe in a higher power to develop your spiritual side.

If you did not grow up in a home that taught the value of having religious or spiritual practices, it may be tough to see a need to develop this aspect of your life now. Maybe you haven't had very positive experiences when it comes to religion and spirituality. Perhaps you have even been let down by God in the past.

It's okay to be skeptical and even critical, though I'd like to challenge you to give the suggestions in this chapter a chance. It's okay to say that you don't agree with

---

[36] See Reachout.com (n.d.) for more information on what spirituality means.

something or that it doesn't work for you, but only after having at least given it a fair try, right? Developing your spiritual side, whether that is based on religion, or on some other, personal beliefs, can benefit you and can aid recovery in the following ways:

1. It can help you forge a new identity.

As you have learned in earlier chapters, you can become so entangled with your eating disorder that you can start to identify with it. You also know that people who have been over-controlled and prevented from making their own decisions, (which is often the case in people with eating disorders) struggle with identity formation.

What religion or spirituality can offer are new beliefs and values that can help shape identity. Do you remember the activity we completed in chapter 3 on values? Exploring values can be a spiritual practice because the essence of spirituality is to create meaning in life, and to live in alignment with what is uniquely meaningful to you.

What you have to be aware of though, if you subscribe to a certain religion, is to not take what some religions teach to the extreme or to use some religious values to justify eating disordered behaviors. For example, some religions value self-control. While self-control can be a positive characteristic to have, it can also become unhealthy. In the case of eating disorders, there is a possibility that it can become toxic because it's easier to take control of food and weight to an extreme.

2. It can help you cope with stress.

In chapter 1, you discovered that one of the ways in which eating disorders are maintained is through emotional dysregulation, or being unable to properly manage emotions. Spiritual practices like prayer, meditation, listening to music, journaling, and creating art can provide a healthy outlet for unpleasant emotions.

3. It can provide a sense of direction and hope.

When your mind is poisoned with eating disordered thoughts, it can be very difficult to see a light at the end of the tunnel. The eating disorder completely takes over and blocks your vision.

Engaging in spiritual or religious practices can, over time, help 'unblock' your vision. That's because when you explore religion and spirituality, you start to learn more about yourself and you desire to live more in line with your true self. You start to derive a new sense of meaning about life, and your hope for the future is restored. You can finally see a life without the need for the things that your eating disorder provides: you learn that you can get these things and better, without it.

My Own Spiritual Journey

My own spiritual journey helped enrich my recovery. God helped me rediscover myself and what was truly important to me. Being a Christian since I was a young girl, I have learned to trust God with so much over the years. At one point, I asked God to show me the way to recovery. I believe He helped guide me to the solutions I came to, many of which are in this book.

I struggled massively with my identity, if you recall the story about my dad and how he parented. I was left without many decision-making skills when I went into the real world, after leaving my parent's home.

I had a lot of painful experiences in my first 5 years away from home, but I didn't realize that anything was obviously missing until it came to my final year of school. It was only then, that I started to think about who I was and about my identity for the first time. I knew that I was successful, intelligent, and capable: I had obtained multiple degrees and I had graduated from nursing school. But still, I struggled to know who I really was.

After my marriage ended in divorce, I re-explored my values and what I wanted out of life. The repeating theme of making decisions that didn't quite feel right in my soul, that were possibly someone else's (AKA, my parents' wishes for me), kept resurfacing and bothering me. My mom always wanted the best for me and I believe that, but I knew that I needed to make sure that the best was what I wanted too, and not my mom's opinion of what was best.

Therapy helped me, as did journaling and researching values and doing exercises on them...but at the end of it all, I prayed. I prayed to God to help me know myself, and to strengthen my identity. I kept hearing that my "identity is in Christ," that He will show you who He is through love and acceptance. I think this is why a spiritual walk with God is so beautiful and enjoyable - we struggle to feel loved and accepted from day to day in the world. God offers unconditional love and acceptance that we cannot do anything to destroy.

I've experienced hardship in my life just like everyone else, but I always experienced a better handling of the hardship when I walked with God and sought his presence and guidance. I walked forward with a strengthened understanding of who I am, what I like, and what my purpose is. After living most of my life asking "is this really what I want, or do I want something else?" due to the way I was brought up, feeling restored in this way gives me indescribable peace.

I am sharing my story, not to try and convert you into a Christian, but purely to open your mind to how a relationship with God, or a spiritual practice can function as a positive force in your life and in your recovery.

I know that many people may have been turned off by religion because of hypocrisy among religious groups, and because of crimes committed in the name of God. It's enough to make anyone nauseated and want to throw it all away.

However, from my own experience of having walked in God's love, and witnessing His amazing work in my life,

I encourage you to think openly and objectively about whether developing your spiritual side may be worth doing, too. After all, we can only develop our own opinion about something if and when we have tried it.

Starting Your Spiritual Journey

To develop your spirituality, you can start by taking baby steps that won't cost you too much time or effort. You don't need to commit to a specific religion, or make drastic changes to become more spiritual. You can test the waters by incorporating small spiritual practices in your daily life. These practices can be anything that brings you comfort and that allow you to connect with God and/or yourself in a meaningful way.

1.) Start your day out with a 'morning routine.'

A morning routine is something that you practice each morning and it involves setting some quiet time aside for yourself. Introducing this private reflection time can help set the tone for the rest of your day. Your morning routine can be whatever you want it to be! Some examples include reading spiritual books, such as the Bible or a devotional, praying for guidance; meditation and thinking about how you'd like your day to unfold; journaling and getting your thoughts down on paper; or simply just sitting with a cup of tea and contemplating all that you are grateful for in your life as it is now.

The purpose of including a morning routine is to get into the habit of making time to connect with God and/or your inner self. In today's modern world, this is something that we don't do nearly enough, yet making time daily, whether it is 10 minutes or 30 minutes, can make a huge difference in helping to ground us in the present.

2.) Pause and Pray.

The second way is to take more pauses, or breaks, throughout the day to 'pray.' Other examples could be taking time out to stretch, reading a few pages of a book in nature, or taking a short walk. When you take regular breaks during the day to do things that make you feel good, you feel more energized, more balanced, and more focused throughout the day.[37]

---

[37] See Dientsman (2019) for more information on how spiritual practices can benefit your life.

3.) Finding a Community.

If there is a religion that you are curious about, for example, Christianity, you can do a Google search to find local churches near you. You could try out one of the services and see how you feel about the religion without having to commit right away. Attending religious gatherings will also allow you to meet people who already subscribe to the religion you're curious about, and who will likely be happy to teach you more about their beliefs and practices.

Similarly, if you'd like to learn more about some other spiritual practices, like meditation and yoga, you can find out about local studios that offer classes. Some may even offer special programs or retreats that are focused on healing.

The great thing about exploring local communities is that you will often find supportive and enthusiastic members who are willing to act as mentors. They can offer you guidance as you move forward in your spiritual journey.

4.) Reading books on Spirituality.

There are many different religious and spiritual books out there that can help you explore your spiritual side without the added 'pressure' of engaging directly with local religious/spiritual communities. Here's an idea to challenge yourself with: find 3 books about spirituality that interest you and read a little of each on alternating days of the week.

5.) Learning Your Values and Living in Alignment with Them.

In chapter 3 you learned all about values and why it is important to explore and identify your core values. You can use your values to inform your daily actions, which will fill your life with meaning each and every day. For example, if one of your core values is helping others, you can live in alignment with this value by looking for ways in which you can help others daily, in small ways. That could be something as simple as offering to make a cup of coffee for your colleague.

Making a conscious effort to help others, if this is one of your core values, is spiritual in a sense. How? Because it is important to you and is something that you firmly and strongly believe in, and that offers a way for you to express your authentic self. These are just a few ideas on how you can become more spiritual by taking small actions.

As you can see, developing your spiritual side doesn't call for immediate, drastic change, and it doesn't mean that you have to commit to a religious belief system. Ultimately, developing your spiritual side is about developing a relationship with God and/or connecting with your inner self, finding your purpose and allowing yourself to be led, which leads to more happiness and a feeling of fulfillment.

How Are Values, Spirituality and Identity Related?

You have learned, so far, that spirituality and religion are about finding meaning in life. You derive meaning from what you value - whether that is the religious beliefs that you subscribe to, or your personal beliefs.

When you spend time reflecting, through religious or spiritual practices, that is when you come to know what is meaningful to you, what you value. That is when you come to know yourself better: how you view yourself, how you view the world, and how you view yourself within the world.

The more time you spend learning and reflecting, the better you become at identifying your core values, and expanding or adjusting them.

This is especially true during recovery. As you recover and grow as a person, your values change because your view of yourself changes too. When you are sick and try to choose your values, they reflect your perspective as a sick person, where you see yourself as a smaller, lower version of yourself, with little hope. As you recover though, you choose values that align with your changing mindset, and that represent your true nature as a healthy and restored person.

I recommend repeating the values exercise in chapter 3 at least once per year, but when going through recovery, at least twice per year, since so much can change in a short period of time!

Remember, values are important because they help guide you with your decision-making and with living life in a way that is true to yourself. It's painful to go down a path where you make decisions that aren't completely your own and to only realize that when you look back. But sometimes you don't know until you know, and that's okay.

I realized I was operating based off of a values system that wasn't completely 'me' for a decade! But I managed to figure it out and find my way back.

Living in line with your values is simple when you discover your truth: every time you make a big decision, look at your values and make sure your decision lines up in the direction of those.

For example, if you have to make a decision to go on a family vacation but there is a work meeting on the Friday that you're supposed to leave, what do you do? Your values lie in family, relationships and connection. Talk to your boss, and see if the meeting can be missed or you can attend virtually, or if someone can take notes for you. Making the decision to spend time with your family when something else important comes up becomes more clear when you look at your values.

Pillar VI:

Nurturing the Physical Body for Recovery.

Chapter 7

Holistic Nutrition for Eating Disorder Recovery

Food, after water, is the single most important element that we need for survival. What we eat, and how much we eat, can influence how we function on both a physical and psychological level. That is why it is so important to understand what good quality nutrition is, as well as the science behind it. This is even more important when you are struggling with an eating disorder because you don't realize how much eating habits and nutrition can actually contribute to your mental state!

I found that quality of nutrition wasn't emphasized in the eating disorder recovery programs I was part of, nor in the many podcasts I listened to, and books that I read. When I did my own research, I realized that I had a lot to learn about nutrition and how my body wanted to be fed. While a tremendous focus on nutrition can quickly become unhealthy, obsessive and carry you away from a focus on what is needed in recovery, it definitely shouldn't be left out. Inside this chapter, you'll find that there is a definitely way to care for yourself through nutrition and honor your recovery process at the same time.

There are plenty of benefits to understanding and being able to apply healthy nutrition concepts during recovery. It is empowering to open your mind to the science behind food and eating because once you understand:

1) how food nourishes your body and helps you function;

2) how your metabolism works:

3) how hunger and satiety function, and

4) how eating disordered behaviors disrupt all of these systems and processes,

When you have a better understanding of these elements, you can start to let go of your fears around controlling food! This chapter is dedicated to helping you understand the foundation of holistic nutrition, so that you can make informed and honoring choices when it comes to what you eat. This is not about introducing you to special diets! I will never categorize foods as "good", "bad", "junk" or "cheat food". This further perpetuates the stigma and virtue around food and takes the focus off of what really matters in life: It is about teaching balance when it comes to food and eating, and making food choices that are nurturing to you specifically, and adopting sustainable ways of eating for the long-term.

The content contained in this chapter is not meant to replace advice that you would get from a dietician or nutritionist. I absolutely suggest and encourage you to visit a specialist as part of your recovery.

Why Do Poor Eating Habits Develop?

It's almost impossible these days to scroll through a magazine, or browse social media and other digital channels without being bombarded with society's ideals of the 'perfect' body type.

Although there seems to be a shift towards more acceptance for different body types and sizes, the status quo still seems to be that, the slimmer a woman is, the more attractive and 'valuable' she is. The reality is, it could take a very long time, and a lot more consistency, for a shift in peoples' perceptions to really take effect in a meaningful way.

It's no wonder then, that in 2021, the diet industry, specifically weight loss services, in the United States, is worth $2.7 billion.[38] When you take a consumerist society, like the United States, which has a 36% obesity rate [39] and you pair it with societal pressure to lose weight, what do you get?

You get a lot of people who want to lose weight...and fast. And service providers who are ready to capitalize on this, hence the invention of fad and yo-yo diets. Unfortunately, providers that promote these kinds of weight loss services don't actually care that much about educating people on proper nutrition. It not only makes their work easier, but also makes their services more marketable when they offer 'quick-fix solutions.' To make matters worse, the sheer volume of these types of providers out there, all trying to set themselves apart, makes it confusing for customers,

---

[38] See IBISWorld (2021) for more information on the diet industry in the United States in 2021.

[39] See World Population Review (2021) for more statistics on obesity rate by country.

who become overwhelmed hearing about hundreds of different diets.

Low-calorie diets are popular, and while they get results in the short-term, they are not sustainable. As you are going to learn, dropping your calorie intake too low, too quickly, can interfere with your metabolism (how you use energy from food), pushing your body into 'starvation mode', and causing you to gain more weight in the long-term. This, in essence, is your body reacting with a stress response to keep yourself alive. The stress hormone, cortisol, is released more often,[40] and even if you aren't eating enough calories to gain weight per traditional nutrition science, your body still has the capability to store energy as fat.[41]

A study that looked at the relationship between obesity rates and eating habits in the United States compared to in France, revealed some very interesting insights about this.[42]

---

[40] See Harris (2015) for more information on cortisol and stress.

[41] See Tomiyama (2010) for more information on the impact of a low calorie diet on the body.

[42] See Powell et al. (2010) for a comparison on eating habits of French and American nationals as they related to obesity rates.

A difference in eating habits between American and French nationals in this particular study seemed to predict the obesity rate for each nation, with Americans having double the rate of obesity than the French.

So what is so different about the way in which these two nations eat? Well, according to this study, Americans tend to try to stick to low calorie diets, and restrict certain types of foods. It seems that, over time, this rigid dieting is too difficult to sustain and for many, it causes them to actually overeat because of trying to maintain a lower than required calorie intake for so long. For the French, they seem to enjoy a variety of foods, and do not restrict any food groups. There is also something telling about the way they eat: they eat slowly, having engaging conversations, and drinking wine between finishing their meals.[38]

This study actually reminds me of a valuable lesson I was taught by my dietician during my eating disorder recovery. My dietician introduced me to the concept of savoring my food by having me eat two delicious chocolates. One chocolate she had me chew up as fast as I could and swallow it, and the second one she said, "make it last as long as possible, almost let it melt in your mouth and notice the taste and how the texture of it is." We both agreed that the second method was a much more enjoyable way to experience food. I always think back to this moment when I'm eating something, and to this day, it helps me fully enjoy what I'm eating. When you can do that, you become satisfied more quickly and have an enjoyable experience with food. You'll find that you don't always want as much of it as you thought you would. It's scary because when you eat your fear foods and give yourself permission to eat them, you step out of your comfort zone. This method of savoring the chocolate taught me that I didn't need to be afraid as I was eating foods that I loved. If I slowed down the process of experiencing a particular food, I would actually enjoy it instead of fearfully rushing through each bite.

Eating Disorders: A Self-Perpetuating Cycle

If we use the term 'self-perpetuating' to describe something, it means that that 'something' has the capacity to keep itself going and growing just because of the nature of it. Eating disorders and the habits they create function in this way.

Take, for example, the starvation that happens in Anorexia Nervosa. How does the state of starvation allow Anorexia Nervosa to continue and get worse? When you're in 'starvation mode', you become more preoccupied with food because you are constantly hungry. If you'll remember, a preoccupation with controlling food, weight, and body shape, is how many eating disorders start. Being in starvation mode by using restriction makes the preoccupation even stronger, and reinforces the initial symptoms. When you lose weight, this also keeps the eating disorder alive because the weight loss provides you with a sense of 'mastery,' positively reinforcing the destructive eating habits.

It doesn't end there: as you have learned, if you restrict calories for a prolonged period of time, it can lead to a break-down in control, resulting in binge-eating. This habit, too, keeps the eating disorder going because now you feel the need to adopt secondary behaviors, like purging, in order to attain the initial 'goal' of losing weight.

This is how eating disorders and the eating habits that go with them can be seen as self-perpetuating cycles: most behaviors make the preoccupation with food, weight and body shape much worse, and increase the need and urge to keep the behaviors going.

How Nutrition and Eating Habits Impact the Body and Mind

What we eat, how much we eat, and other eating habits, have far-reaching consequences for our minds and bodies. To illustrate this, I'm going to tell you about an eye-opening study that was conducted in 1944 by Keys and Brozek in Minnesota, known as the "Minnesota Starvation Experiment."[43]

The Minnesota Starvation Experiment was conducted during the time that World War 2 was going on, when hunger and starvation were rife[43]. The researchers, Keys and Brozek (1944) wanted to know how to help people recover from starvation, and they wanted to learn about the psychological and physiological effects of being in starvation mode.[39]

They took 36 male volunteers and studied them for about a year. In the first three months of the study, they had the men eat over 3000 calories a day, then for six months, they put them on a semi-starvation diet, which was much less caloric intake.[39] In the final phase, or the three month

---

43 See Keys & Brozek (1944) as cited in Baker & Keramidas (2013) for more details about the Minnesota Starvation Experiment.

rehabilitation phase, the men had their calories increased to an amount similar to the first phase. The results provided a peek into what people experiencing eating disorders face on a psychological and physiological level.

During the semi-starvation phase, the men became preoccupied with food.[44] They spoke about food, read books about food and even dreamed about food.[40] Some of the men experienced concentration issues, finding it hard to focus on anything other than food and eating.[40] The men also developed body image concerns, and participants who were extroverted before they went on the semi-starvation diet became more withdrawn, and felt socially inadequate during the semi-starvation and rehabilitation phases.[40] In both the semi-starvation and rehabilitation phases, more symptoms of depression and anxiety were observed, and interpersonal relationships suffered: the men tended to become more easily irritated and sensitive in their interactions with others.[40]

At the physiological level, during the rehabilitation period, many of the men binge-ate, or ate uncontrollably, and

---

[44] See Gil (n.d.) for more details about the findings from the Minnesota Starvation Experiment.

they also found it hard to recognize hunger and fullness cues.[40] After a long period of semi-starvation, they felt hungrier and binging and purging were present as far as 5 months into the refeeding/rehabilitation phase.[40] In addition to weight changes, the men experienced physical symptoms, like gastrointestinal problems, light-headedness; less need for sleep, headaches, and sensitivity to the cold.[40]

The mens' basal metabolic rates significantly declined during the semi-starvation phase. Basal metabolic rate refers to the amount of calories the body needs to function when at rest. When you restrict food and your body goes into starvation mode, your body weight drops, you need less calories to maintain your lower weight, but it also means that your body burns less calories. Over time, starvation mode can slow your metabolism down, which is why, when people go on low calorie diets, they often end up putting all the weight back on, plus more. In the semi-starvation phase, men lost 25% of their weight, 40% of which was muscle. That's because in starvation mode, your body is lacking in critical reserves and it starts to use the protein in your muscles as fuel to survive.

The Minnesota Starvation Study[39] illustrates that eating disorder behaviors like restriction can influence binge-eating, and also shows how it can impact the minds and bodies of sufferers.

Note: While you may be concerned about putting on weight, you can rest assured that your metabolism will eventually recover and return to functioning normally once you start eating healthily again.

I personally understand that reaching that place of balance is one of the most challenging pieces of recovery. I can remember how difficult this felt. The rule of thumb you can always return to is that regularized, appropriate, nutrient-dense nutrition will create balance in your body. As a result, the stress inside of your body will decrease and your body will start to heal. This includes your metabolism and your body's ability to use all nutrients for a purpose!

Nutritional Basics for Healing

There is so much more to nutrition than just calories or macronutrients (a.k.a "macros")! But when you have an eating disorder, these are all that seem to matter. Controlling your food when you have an eating disorder is about striving to be thinner, or to have a "perfect" physique. When the primary goal is just on aesthetics and not the health status of the inside of your body, holistic health gets put on the back burner.

But what if you looked at nutrients in a different way? What if you understood calories and macronutrients as critical fuel that your body uses to help you function and thrive? Besides calories supplying your body with fuel to function, calories from different macronutrients and micronutrients support multiple bodily processes, and also help protect you against ill health.

When you supply your body with the nutrients that it needs, in helpful quantities, you will also find that your cravings for non-nutritious foods declines. The types of foods you eat play a big role in you feeling hungry later on, and in you feeling fuller for longer.

In this next part of the book, you'll hear about:

1) what macronutrients and micronutrients are

2) How macro and micronutrients sustain life;

3) about hunger and satiation, especially what contributes to each;

4) gut health and why restoring gut health is crucial for recovery and wellbeing; and

5) what mindful eating means

What are Macronutrients and Micronutrients?

Macronutrients are nutrients that our bodies require in large amounts. They are known as carbohydrates, fats and protein. Micronutrients are needed in smaller amounts by our bodies, and these are what you would know as vitamins and minerals. Both macronutrients and micronutrients are essential for good health. Let's take a closer look at **macronutrients:**

1) Carbohydrates.

Carbohydrates are the body's preferred fuel source.[45] They provide the body with sustained energy, they help preserve muscle mass, and they also fuel our brains.[41] Grains

---

[45] See Washington State University (n.d.) for more information on macronutrients and how they function in the body.

are high in carbohydrates, as are fruits, and some vegetables (especially more starchy vegetables, like potatoes).

Carbs get a bad reputation for causing weight gain, and that's because of how certain types of carbohydrates are digested and how they impact hunger and satiation. Not all carbohydrates are created equal, though, and we need a substantial amount of the fibrous carbohydrates in our diets to keep our bodies functioning as they should!

To explain it simply, carbohydrates may be refined or unrefined, that is, they may be processed or unprocessed. The types of carbohydrates that get a bad rep are the refined, or processed ones - these are the ones we need to be mindful of. "Mindful" doesn't mean cutting them out, but rather increasing the unprocessed, whole food versions to "crowd out" the processed and refined versions. Processed carbohydrates don't offer a rich nutrient profile in the way of nutrition, and are often un-filling and leave us wanting more. Refined carbs should not be labeled as "bad", but I encourage you to look at these types of foods with curiosity, and ask what amount of them is honoring to your body and the healing journey you are on as an individual.

What happens with refined carbohydrates during processing is that they are stripped of their nutrients, so their original health benefits become void. They are also digested quickly, which causes a 'spike' and then a drop in blood sugar levels. This is what is responsible for cravings and feelings of hunger fairly soon after eating this version of carbohydrates.[46] Packaged foods such as crackers, cookies, some pastas, white rice, and breakfast cereals are examples of processed, refined carbohydrates.

Whole food and minimally processed carbohydrates, on the other hand, are nutrient-dense, take longer to digest, and depending on their glycemic index (which we will explore later), can help us feel fuller for longer. These are the kinds of carbohydrates that offer more minerals, vitamins, water and fiber. Examples of minimally processed, whole food carbohydrate sources include fruit, oats, potatoes, brown rice, wild rice, pinto beans, black beans, sourdough breads, and fresh vegetables.

I remember how I used to associate baked goods as 'bad' for weight management because of what I always

---

[46] See Bjarnadottir (2017) for more information on the digestion of carbohydrates.

seemed to hear. Labeling foods as good or bad is not helpful, and can lead to obsessing over certain foods, restricting certain foods, and other eating disorder behaviors. Just because a food you love is not the greatest choice for the body, it doesn't mean you need to avoid it at all costs. But yes, there are indeed truths about the connection between eating large amounts of processed foods and poor health. When we frequently eat food that is lacking in rich nutrients, our body *does* start to go down pathways of disease and dysfunction because it doesn't have what it needs to maintain its health. That is why focusing on crowding out processed foods by bringing in the nutrient-dense foods provides a solution to a balanced relationship with food and the health of your body.

Another thing that changed the game for me in recovery was learning how to make baked goods with different, upgraded ingredients. You can begin doing this yourself by swapping your traditional sweeteners out for monk fruit extract, stevia, and allulose when making cookies and muffins. These sweeteners are different because even though they add delicious sweetness, they do not have an effect on the blood sugar. A swap for all-purpose flour is for every ¾ cup of all-purpose flour, use 1 1/2 cups of almond flour. The almond flour has dietary fat, which helps you feel satisfied sooner than eating a product with regular wheat flour. I began doing this when healing my body from binge-eating, and from the pre-diabetes that I developed during years of binge-eating food. This baking technique allowed me to use satisfying, whole food ingredients that improved my health while enjoying treats I loved at the same time. This was revolutionary in my recovery because it offered a sustainable way of eating. That was something I had never experienced in my adult life before!

As you can imagine, you can't perfectly imitate the buttery, flaky flavorful texture of a croissant. Ironically, this is a French food - and a lot of French food is rich and delicious. This was a reason to help me feel excited and hopeful that if the French can eat in a balanced way with these decadent, wonderful foods that I was afraid of, so could I!

During my recovery, I had to come to grips with the fact that most of my dietary choices were packaged, frozen, and processed foods. I decided to give my food choices a makeover in the name of self-love and care. I wanted to see progress in my life with my binge-eating habits, and I knew that my current way of eating was contributing to the issue. Within 6 weeks of practicing crowding out processed choices with more fruits, vegetables, wholesome dietary fats, low glycemic sweeteners and carbohydrates, I had completely forgotten about my eating disorder and looked back in shock at the whole situation. How was it that I hadn't even had a binge in 6 weeks?! I was beyond thrilled and it was one of the happiest times of my life!

2) Protein.

Protein is a macronutrient that plays an important role in the building and recovery of bodily tissue. Say you broke a bone: protein would be vital in repairing the bone by rebuilding bone tissue. Protein is also required for proper functioning of the body's hormonal systems, as well as metabolism.[41] Special transport proteins help in the movement of nutrients to the right tissues.[41]

A person's protein needs depend on how active they are, as well as their current weight. We need at least 0.36g of protein per pound of body weight[47] to maintain muscle mass and vital bodily functions.

---

47 See Healthline (n.d.) for more information on protein requirements in the diet.

Including protein in the diet can also help with feelings of hunger and satiation, and we will explore this more later. Protein sources include animal products; legumes; soy products; nuts; seeds; and whole grains.

3) Fats.

Fats provide energy, just like carbohydrates and protein do. Fat is unique because the body has the ability to store it in case there is a 'crisis' and food supplies are low, or if there is stress inside the body from disease or hormonal imbalances, to give you an example. The body can only store a certain amount of glucose, the broken down component of carbohydrates, inside of the liver and muscles. Fat can be stored in larger amounts in the body.

Fat acts as padding for vital organs, protecting them from damage. It also provides insulation, and helps regulate body temperature. Fats are crucial for the absorption of certain vitamins, namely vitamins A, D, E, and K.[48] Fat, because it stays in our systems for longer and takes longer to digest, also helps with satiety control.

---

[48] See Clifford & Kozil (n.d.) for more information on fat soluble vitamins.

Fats should make up 25% of our diets at a minimum. This might sound like more than you're used to hearing, but it is for good reason! If our diets are too low in fat, it tends to make us more susceptible to giving into cravings, and to think less clearly. Fat provides satiation value and nourishes our brain cells. Fat molecules are important in the development of hormones, and in keeping our cell walls intact. They offer more calories per gram than carbohydrates and protein.[41] Sources of fats include oils, nuts, seeds, avocado, dairy, oily fish, cheese, and meat.

Just like unrefined carbohydrates that are considered healthy and better than refined carbohydrates, some fats are considered healthy, while others are considered less healthy or even harmful.

Unsaturated fats are fats, like olive oil, are typically liquid at room temperature, but are also found in solid and semi-solid foods like fatty fish, nuts, seeds, and nut butters.[49] Saturated fats are usually solid at room temperature, and include butter, cheese, coconut oil, and fatty cuts of meat[52].

---

[49] See Tinsley (2020) for more information on different sources of saturated, unsaturated and trans fats.

Trans fats are fats that are liquid, but when processed, become solid.

There is still some debate regarding the different types of fats and how they nourish or harm the body. Trans-saturated fats are inflammatory, and are found in fast food and commercially packaged, processed foods. Inflammation for prolonged periods can cause your body to become sick, or even develop a chronic disease.

Some studies argue that consuming a lot of saturated fats has been linked to greater risk of heart disease[45] by increasing a person's level of LDL (low density lipoprotein), which are the small, sticky molecules of cholesterol that can block arteries. The main thing, however, is to remember that not all saturated fat is created equal: Saturated fat found in conventionally-raised cows is inflammatory due to the nature of the cow's life. They are fed genetically modified foods, given antibiotics and other substances in order to increase the amount of meat they can provide. These additives and their compounds become part of the meat that is used from the cow. When eaten by humans, these additives are not recognized by the human body as natural, and are toxic and inflammatory. On the other hand, saturated fats found from organic, grass-fed, grass-finished beef and coconut oil will provide cleaner fuel for our bodies. Unsaturated fats, found in avocados, almonds, pecans and hazelnuts, help lower LDL cholesterol, lower inflammation, and build cell membranes.[45] Eating unsaturated fats has been associated with heart health. Trans fats have been linked to the worst health outcomes because they not only raise LDL cholesterol, but also lower the high density lipoprotein (known as HDL) cholesterol, hugely increasing the risk for heart disease.[50] It's important to paint the picture that we are all individuals, and we all have unique dietary needs and preferences. The way our food is prepared, all the way from its origin until it comes into our body, has an effect on the inside functioning of our bodies at a cellular level. When choosing fats to include in your diet, choose organic, cold-pressed oils like coconut and olive oil. Opt for grass-fed butter, cheese, ghee, beef tallow, organic nuts, nut butters, coconuts, and avocados. Limit consumption of canola oil, vegetable oils, and seed oils, as well as processed, conventional sources of fat found in fast foods and packaged food as these have more inflammatory properties once inside the body.

---

[50] See Mayo Clinic (n.d.) for more information on bad versus good cholesterol.

If you have never heard of cholesterol, or have heard of it but don't really know what it is, cholesterol is a waxy-like substance in the body. Our bodies need cholesterol to make cells, produce hormones, and to help our metabolisms function efficiently.[51] However, having a higher ratio of LDL cholesterol to HDL cholesterol is harmful because it can build up, block arteries and lead to a heart attack or stroke. [47]

During my journey with healing from binge-eating, I developed pre-diabetes from the frequent and large consumption of sugary, processed foods during my binges. What I didn't know then, is these frequent blood sugar spikes caused my body to be less sensitive to the hormone insulin, and my blood sugar levels stayed elevated for longer periods of time. This caused inflammation, and put stress on the inside of my body. The hormone insulin is made by the pancreas, and is secreted when we eat. The more carbohydrates and sugar we eat, the more insulin we need to help the blood sugar get into our cells so the body can use this as fuel for life. It was complicated to heal my body from pre-diabetes when I was still sick with a binge-eating

---

[51] See the American Heart Association (2020) for more information on how cholesterol affects the body.

disorder. I knew the behavior needed to stop, but I didn't know how to do that at the beginning. In order to heal my body from pre-diabetes, I had to begin making more mindful choices about the types of carbohydrates and sweeteners I ate. That is why I found such freedom in choosing upgraded, glycemic friendly ingredients like monk fruit extract, almond flour and coconut flour. I was able to eat what I enjoyed and heal my body at the same time! I know that there are others struggling with this problem as well, and that's why I've included the importance of blood sugar balance and how to get started with it. To lower inflammation inside the body, it's important to maintain proper blood sugar balance and a good ratio of HDL to LDL cholesterol in the blood. You can find out the status of your cholesterol and lipid profile by getting blood drawn at the doctor's office.

To go back to different types of fats, unsaturated fats are fats that are typically liquid at room temperature, for example olive oil, but are also found in solid and semi-solid foods like fatty fish, nuts, seeds, and nut butters.[52] Saturated fats are usually solid at room temperature, and include butter, cheese, coconut oil, and fatty cuts of meat[52]. Trans

---

[52] See Tinsley (2020) for more information on different sources of saturated, unsaturated and trans fats.

fats are fats that are liquid, but when processed, become solid.

Now that you have a better idea about what macronutrients are and about why they are important, let's turn to micronutrients.

Micronutrients

Micronutrients consist of the 13 essential vitamins and the 13 essential minerals that our bodies require to function correctly.[53] These essential vitamins and minerals perform multiple roles in the body, including preserving immune health, and ensuring healthy skin, muscle, and bone. They are crucial for metabolism as well.

Although we only need vitamins and minerals in small amounts, deficiencies can lead to disease. For example, a severe vitamin C deficiency can cause scurvy, a disease that breaks down connective tissue in skin, bones,

---

53 See Bolt (2015) for more information on micronutrients and how they function in the body.

blood vessels, tendons, and muscles, and a deficiency in vitamin A can cause blindness.[54]

The main difference between vitamins and minerals is that minerals do not break down when exposed to heat, air, or acid, so they are more easily absorbed by the body through the foods we consume. Whereas vitamins may be broken down through cooking/storage methods.[55]

To get all of the essential vitamins and minerals that our bodies need, and to prevent illness and disease, we need to eat a diet that includes a lot of variety. To demonstrate this, a table on the next page identifies these micronutrients, their function in the body, as well as what foods they can be found in.

---

[54] See Brennan (2021) for more information on the impact of vitamin deficiencies on the body.

[55] See Spritzler & Arnarson (2019) for information on how cooking affects the nutrient content of food.

Vitamin	Purpose	Where to Find it
Vitamin A	Provides strengthened immunity, helps fight off infections, improves vision and skin health	Dark leaky green vegetables, spinach, broccoli, carrots, pumpkin, liver, fish, kidney, yogurt, eggs
Vitamin D	Helps the body absorb calcium along w/ vitamin K, helps strengthen bones and teeth, regulates mood	Sunlight, supplementation, cod liver oil, milk, eggs, liver
Vitamin E	Helps maintain cell structure and protects cell membranes	whole grains, peanut butter, tomatoes, eggs
Vitamin K	Helps with blood clotting and delivering calcium to bones	Spinach, Lettuce, Kale, cauliflower, cabbage, broccoli, fish, liver, eggs, meat
B Vitamins (thiamine, folate, riboflavin, niacin, pantothenic acid, biotin, B6, and B12)	Helps support blood cell formation and helps the body convert energy from food, Helps keep eyes, skin and nervous system healthy,	millet, sorghum, beans, peas, eggs, liver, meat, mi k, fresh fruit, green leafy vegetables, whole grains
Vitamin C	Helps with wound healing and skin health, Supports the immune system	Citrus fruits like oranges, lemons, grapefruit, green pepper, tomato, broccoli, potatoes

Table 3

Mineral	Purpose	Where to Find It
Iron	Helps make red blood cells that carry oxygen around the body	liver, meat, beans, eggs, dark green leafy vegetables, parsley
Calcium	Important in heart muscle function and bodily muscle contraction. Helps develop strong bones and teeth	Milk, cheese, green leafy vegetables, cabbage, okra
Iodine	Helps with produce thyroid hormone	Supplementation, seaweeds, fish, dairy
Sodium	Helps fluid balance in the body and has an important role in muscle contraction	pink himalayan sea salt, table salt
Potassium	Plays an important role in muscle contraction, fluid balance, and nerve impulse conduction	Sweet potatoes, avocados, bananas, beets, dates, nuts
Magnesium	Helps support muscle relaxation, DNA and antioxidant creation	Dark green leafy vegetables, whole grains, legumes, seeds
Chloride	Works with sodium to maintain fluid balance in	Salt, celery, tomato, lettuce

	the body, helps make stomach acid.	
Phosphorus	Helps form healthy bones and teeth. Helps with muscle contraction.	Meats, poultry, fish, beans, seeds, dairy
Zinc	Helps with cell division and wound healing. If Zinc is low, the Immune system can be affected	Oysters, red meat, nuts, poultry, whole grain
Selenium	Helps repair cell damage caused by free radicals and oxidative stress	Brazil nuts, seaweed, seafood, organ meats
Manganese	Helps with macronutrient breakdown and cell division.	Whole grains, nuts, soy products
Sulfur	Helps fight off unhelpful bacteria and helps repair DNA	Seafood, soy beans, kidney beans, black beans, nuts
Copper	Helps Iron to be absorbed from the gut	Chocolate, liver, shellfish, wheat bran

Table 4

When you eat a variety of foods and a balanced diet that includes these micronutrients, you will feel noticeably different, both physically and mentally. That's because your body and mind will be well-nourished and able to perform properly. I didn't learn the importance of rotating in these foods in both of the tables provided until I was well into my recovery. If I would have begun incorporating these sooner, I may have reaped the benefit of early healing! Organ meats and seaweed were odd foods to me that I've only just started to eat in the last year. I choose to eat them for the benefit of vitamins and minerals they provide. It's really important to me to feel my best and function at the top of my game. You can certainly supplement, but the benefit of supplementing vitamins and minerals is different for each person. Like in other parts of the book, I'll encourage you to experiment with supplementation, and then try eating a variety of these foods in your diet. See what works for you and makes you feel your best.

Energy Requirements

Energy or calorie requirements differ according to a person's age, gender, and physical activity levels. You might be searching for numbers here, but I firmly believe that focusing on calories when healing from an eating disorder can become an obsession and distract your focus away from actually feeding your body based on how full or hungry it feels.

Babies and young children require significantly less calories than adolescents who are growing quickly; and adults, who are fully grown. Also, because men typically have larger bodies than women (they are usually taller and have more muscle tissue), they need more calories than women do, to sustain these larger bodies.

Energy requirements slowly decline from age 26+ as metabolism slows down, muscle is lost, and as full growth has been attained. [56] Many factors affect someone's energy requirements and metabolic rate. Working an active job, being on your feet regularly for prolonged periods of time, weight lifting, and other physical activity increase the body's energy demands. Muscle tissue has higher energy requirements, and will need a slightly higher caloric intake to maintain.

---

[56] See Dietary Guidelines for Americans (2010) for more information on typical calorie requirements according to age and gender.

As someone with an eating disorder, it can be illuminating and helpful to visit a professional dietician specialized in eating disorders. Only a qualified professional can give you unique advice on the energy requirements that you need for your specific body type.

What to Expect when you Visit a Dietician

I would highly recommend that, as part of your recovery, you visit a professional dietician or nutritionist specializing in eating disorders. These types of professionals can help you become better educated about nutrition, and become more healthy and well-nourished by offering you guidance about nutrition and food, taking the eating disorder into consideration.

In my own experience, visiting a dietician helped me when it came to talking about the emotional charge and labels I used to assign to certain foods, it also helped me break down barriers I had when it came to eating my fear foods, like pizza! I was taught how to eat mindfully which helped me enjoy my food more, which was the beginning of my journey of learning to listen to my body and recognize when I was feeling full.

When you first visit a dietician or nutritionist, they'll take a look at your eating habits as well as what you eat. They might weigh you and measure your height to determine your body mass index (BMI). Your BMI is a calculation performed by a dietician to classify you as either underweight, at a healthy weight, overweight, or obese according to your age and gender. [57] If you visit a dietician specializing in eating disorder recovery or use a "Health at Every Size Approach", it's likely that BMI will not be utilized as a marker for weight or health at all. This is because BMI readings have their limitations, and do not always deliver accurate markers for health per individual. Getting my BMI results at the doctor's office was always triggering for me, and often threw me off track of healing for weeks to months. As someone with an eating disorder, you might find it triggering to know your weight or BMI, which category you fall into, so if you feel that this may be the case, you can let the dietician know beforehand, asking them to refrain from not to sharing these numbers with you and providing feedback on your weight. There are scenarios where discussion about weight is necessary for medical

---

[57] See NHLBI (n.d.) for more information on body mass index and how it is calculated.

safety, and your medical professional will definitely be honest with you about this.

Even if the dietician does not disclose your stats, they can still be helpful in advising you on what foods to include in your diet, as well as in helping to challenge the way in which you view different types of foods, as in my case.

A simple Google search will help you find the right dietician or nutrition coach for you. There are many of us out there who specialize in eating disorder recovery, and some key-words that you might want to look out for include 'intuitive eating,' 'mindful eating,' and a 'health at every size approach.'

Hunger and Satiety

In eating disorders, where controlling food and eating is a constant struggle, learning about what makes us experience hunger to begin with, as well as what makes us feel full can help with making better food choices and with adapting eating habits.

Although with eating disorders binge-eating is often triggered by distressing emotions, we cannot downplay the role of nutrition in inducing hunger. If you eat foods that lack nutrition and that do not promote satiety, then you'll find that you get hungry more often.

Earlier, we talked about refined carbohydrates like cookies, crackers, breads and some pastas? I mentioned that they digest quickly, causing your blood sugar to rise rapidly and then drop. If you include more of this kind of carbohydrate and your blood sugar is constantly spiking and dropping throughout the day, the truth is that you are going to have a super tough time feeling satisfied. Most of the time you'll feel hungry quickly after eating them, and you'll think about this kind of food more often. It's not actually a mental battle: it's the physical. It's the scientific properties of this food and its impact on blood sugar that causes you to feel the craving.

Focusing on including more unrefined carbohydrates, like fruits, vegetables, legumes and wholegrains, will keep you feeling fuller for much longer.[58] You may also remember that I mentioned something called the glycemic index. I'll explain:

---

[58] See Elliot (2021) for more information on how eating too many unrefined carbohydrates can contribute to feeling more hungry more often.

As you have learned already, refined carbohydrates spike your blood glucose levels, but the extent to which this happens depends on the specific carbohydrate. The glycemic index is a number that is assigned to carbohydrates that indicates the extent to which a certain carbohydrate will spike your blood glucose. Having this knowledge allows you to make choices for carbohydrates that have a low glycemic index more often.

Carbohydrates that have a glycemic index of 55 and lower are considered low glycemic index foods, whereas those with a glycemic index of 70 and above are considered high glycemic foods.[59] As an example, oatmeal has a glycemic index of 55, while breakfast cereals like Cheerios have a glycemic index of 80+.

What else can you do to add satiety? Foods that promote feelings of satiety, besides low glycemic carbohydrates, include healthy fats and protein. You can add in some protein and fat to each meal or snack so you're providing your body with a balance of different types of energy.

---

59 See Dansinger (2021) for more details on the glycemic index of different foods.

We talked a little about this earlier, but a diet that is very low in fat (particularly saturated fat), has a tendency to make you feel hungry more often.[55] Fat takes a long time to digest and releases fullness-promoting hormones. Also, when your diet is too low in fat, it can cause you to crave carbohydrates and sweet foods. Omega-3 fatty acids found in fatty fish like salmon are examples of supplements and foods you can add in during your journey of stabilizing your appetite and energy levels while also keeping you fuller for longer.

Eating enough protein also helps with feelings of fullness by reducing hunger hormones and increasing hormones that let your body know you're full.[55] Protein is quite calorie and nutrient dense too, and you'll likely feel full sooner when you include it.

Fiber is that part of plant foods, like fruits, vegetables and wholegrains which our bodies are unable to digest. Since fiber is indigestible, it adds bulk to our diets, and helps promote healthy bowel movements. It can also, like low glycemic carbohydrates, keep blood sugar levels stable, as it slows the rate at which sugar is absorbed by the body. Since high-fiber foods slow digestion, they make you feel fuller for longer.[55]

If you're recovering from prolonged food restriction and are going through a 're-feeding' phase, it can feel like you're always hungry no matter how much you eat. This will balance out over time. It is uncomfortable both mentally and physically, but by taking it a meal at a time, and by applying the other pillars of recovery, you will get through this time in your life. Including more fat and as many nutrient-dense foods we discussed earlier in this chapter, you can induce the feeling of being satisfied while healing your body. Our bodies become sick and stressed on the inside when they don't get regular nutrition. By loving on it and giving it amazing, nutritious food, you'll find how rewarding recovery is.

To recap, you can promote feelings of satiation by:

- Eating more nutrient dense foods, like unrefined carbohydrates, healthy fats, and protein.

- Including more fiber in your diet.

- Eating mindfully by slowing down and savoring each bite.

Chapter 8

The Importance of Gut Health in Recovery

The link between gut health and mental health may not strike the average person as something 'obvious,' but recent research has established that there is indeed a causal relationship between the two.[60] The way in which the gut and the brain communicate with and influence one another has been termed the 'gut-brain axis.'[60]

Problems for mental health occur when there is an imbalance in 'good' versus 'bad' bacteria in the gut, as well as inflammation in the gut, and this has been linked to anxiety and depression . As humans, we have trillions of microbes, or bacteria living in our digestive tract and having enough of the good kind is very important for mental

---

[60] See Clapp et al. (2017), and Navarro-Tapia et al. (2021) for more information on the brain, gut and mental health.

wellness. That's because good bacteria in the gut release GABA, an amino acid which acts as a neurotransmitter in the brain, and which helps us calm down and relax.

Fortunately, there are steps we can take to encourage the growth of good bacteria in the gut, and these include consuming probiotic and prebiotic foods.

Probiotic foods are living bacteria that add to the good bacteria already in our guts. Probiotic foods to incorporate are kimchi, which is nearly an everyday-staple in the Korean diet and consists of salted and fermented vegetables; natto, which is a fermented soybean food eaten in Japanese culture; kefir, which is a fermented yogurt drink; refrigerated sauerkraut; and refrigerator pickles.

Prebiotic foods are those foods that are rich in prebiotic fibers. These help nourish the digestive tissue and gut microbiota so that they can do their job for the body. They are actually indigestible to humans as energy, but available as food for healthy gut bacteria. Prebiotic foods to incorporate include raw jicama; raw green bananas; allulose; inulin; acacia fiber; onion; garlic; leek; dandelion greens; asparagus; radishes; avocado; coconut oil; chia seeds; and golden flax seeds.

Incorporating both probiotic and prebiotic foods in a gut-healing regimen is important because we not only want to introduce a variety of good bacteria to the digestive system, we want to feed them something so they can stay alive and thrive, giving us the benefits of a healthy gut microbiome (a healthy balance of good gut bacteria).

There are also many probiotic supplements out there that can be a beneficial addition to your gut health regimen. Including these was an essential part of my recovery process because it helped balance out the way I was craving food by adding helpful bacteria into my digestive system. With years of disordered eating and irregular nutrition habits, my gut tissue and gut microbiota were damaged and needed healing. When I began shifting my focus with nutrition and had the perspective of "adding in" or "crowding out" higher glycemic foods and eating a higher dietary fat content, it helped my gut tissue heal and my skin, mood and eating disorder symptoms completely healed.

How to Choose the Right Probiotic Supplements

When beginning probiotic supplements, it's important to know that not all are created equal. It is best to choose a product that has 5-7 strains of bacteria versus just one, as the goal in creating a healthy balance in the gut is to aim for diversity.

I would recommend choosing a supplement with excellent reviews. In fact, during my recovery, I decided to invest in myself and purchased a product that helped me with my cravings and appetite, which was an enormous gift living through bulimia. I stopped thinking about food 24/7. It helped me with satiation, better mood and better hunger and fullness cues. It helped promote regular digestive patterns and my skin rashes went away. It elevated my mood: I felt like someone had taken me out of a dungeon and brought me to a sunny place. It wasn't that I was in a good mood for just one day, now, I was in a good mood all of the time.

In my own experience, before I began to add healthful habits into my life, before I began including foods my body needed me to eat, and before paying attention to gut health, I couldn't apply intuitive eating (eating based on hunger and fullness cues). My theory is that I had good intentions: I wanted to eat intuitively, but I had a lot of blood-sugar fluctuations affecting my mood and energy levels, and cravings caused by these different elements that kept me from successfully adopting intuitive eating. Gut healing was crucial to my recovery in so many ways.

As a Health Coach, I am qualified to advise my clients on gut health and to help with gut healing. I've created a quiz on my website that acts as a screening tool for gut health! You can get your results at www.vitalitycoaching.org by taking the quiz on the front page of the website.

Chapter 9

Mindful Eating

Do you remember the story of how my dietician got me to eat the two chocolates, eating the one as fast as possible, and savoring the other one? In the second scenario, I was more 'present' with my food, I was paying attention to the smell of the chocolate, how it tasted, and the texture of it as it melted in my mouth.

When your awareness is focused on what is happening in the present moment like this, it means that you are being 'mindful.' This is the opposite of what typically happens when you binge-eat, or when you eat to manage your emotions.

The purpose of mindful eating in eating disorder recovery then, is to have you focus on the moment, by being conscious of the sensory experience of eating, helping you to enjoy and savor your food.[61] What this does is it helps you to better tune in to your body: when you are highly aware, it is easier to sense when you have had enough to eat and eating becomes a more positive, enjoyable experience.

So, now that you understand what mindful eating is and how it can be helpful, I want to challenge you to practice the following mindful eating practice:

1. Next time you are going to eat a meal, before you even eat the meal, notice the food on your plate.

2. Notice the colors, the smell, and the texture of the food - just observe - don't judge it or make any comments, just use your senses to examine it.

3. When you eat the food, take your time chewing it slowly, notice the different subtle tastes, and textures.

How did this experience go for you? Write down 3 things that you noticed when eating your food in this way.

---

[61] See Nelson (2017) for more information on mindful eating.

Chapter 10

Re-Imagining Physical Activity and Movement

Movement, exercise and physical activity are important as part of living a healthy, balanced life, and I invite you to include this into your recovery process! You can look at incorporating physical activity into your life as part of a lifestyle change, and not something temporary, or a quick way to lose weight and change your body. This mentality places stress on your body as weight fluctuates quickly, and the focus is not on keeping your body healthy for life, but rather fixated on a momentary pleasure that doesn't provide lasting satisfaction.

The benefits to staying physically active on a regular basis are exponential. Exercise helps improve your mood, sleep and metabolic health, which means having an optimal balance of blood sugar and cholesterol, reducing your risk for developing heart disease and diabetes. It is also the key to living a longer, better quality life and feel happy.

As you learned in chapter one, exercise may be used by some people struggling with eating disorders as another way to try to control weight, shape and body size. So, it can be a sensitive aspect to navigate during recovery. That's because exercise, for some of you, may not be associated with the positive benefits mentioned. Instead, exercise may be thought of as 'punishment' for overeating, or as a kind of 'means to an end,' that end being to lose as much weight as possible.

If you hold this perspective, it's important to shift your mindset about exercise. Exercise is more enjoyable when viewed as a way to take care of yourself and maintain health. It shouldn't feel like a chore. If it feels this way, it's likely you aren't enjoying the type of exercise you are engaging in. It's time to bring new things into your routine! Oftentimes, people with eating disorders who are aiming to lose weight engage in a lot of cardio, and let's face it, not many people enjoy walking on a treadmill for 2 hours!

Instead of thinking about exercise with the ultimate goal being to lose weight, see if you can think of some other positive reasons for exercising regularly. Here are some examples:

- Aerobic exercise that gets your heart pumping, like jogging, dancing, and swimming, is great for heart health and reduces the risk of cardiovascular and brain disease as you age. It also releases feel-good endorphins that act as a natural 'antidepressant' and boost your mood.

- Resistance training, or training with weights supports bone and muscle health and keeps you strong as you get older. The more strength you build up and muscle you maintain, the more mobility you will have when you get older, and the better your quality of life will be.

- Workout classes can be a great place to socialize and meet like-minded people who enjoy similar hobbies!

- Exercise doesn't have to be conventional - you don't need to go to the gym or go to classes, you can make exercise an adventure and it doesn't need to cost you anything. Go for a hike or for a walk along the beach if you love nature and have access to it. This is a form of therapy in itself.

Can you think of any other benefits of exercise, or any other ways that you can shift your current thinking? Write these down! Now, as a closing activity, come up with just one exercise, or physical activity-related goal for your recovery. This should be a small and simple goal and it should align with a healthy view of exercise and its associated benefits. Avoid making a goal that is focused on weight loss, but rather make it about the benefits of what a living life in a fit body would be like for you. Focusing on the feeling of what you want to experience will get you in touch with new ways you can work on moving toward your desires. You might write down "I want to feel strong, sexy, confident". You might picture that version of you being able to run 2 miles without difficulty. Perhaps you want to feel more confident walking around the pool in a bathing suit. These desires and feelings are not wrong, and I encourage you not to stuff them down! We don't have to give up our desires to be in shape when we're recovering from an eating disorder. We *do* have to know that our desires are coming from the right place, a place of wanting to be happy, healthy and feel confident in ourselves, and aren't going to put us on a damaging path. With a combination of making mindset shifts and small lifestyle changes, physical activity is bound to become a source of joy and excitement in your recovered life!

Pillar VII:

Mental Toughness & Resilience

Chapter 11

Upgrade Your Coping Skills

In chapter 1, you learned about self-monitoring and how it can help create awareness of your emotional and situational triggers. You also learned about how you can reframe your thoughts, which has the potential to influence how you feel and act.

This is a great technique to master, but sometimes, you may need some additional tools when reframing doesn't work, or even to strengthen your resistance to engage in eating disordered behaviors.

In the first part of this chapter, I'll introduce you to more strategies that you can add to your toolkit. These are going to help when it comes to stopping your old behaviors in their tracks, and preventing a complete relapse, too!

The Art of Distraction

Distraction can be a useful tool to use to help delay or stop your eating disorder behaviors. It is important to remember, though, that distraction usually provides temporary relief or a temporary solution. You still need to keep working on challenging your core beliefs about yourself through self-monitoring and reframing, working with a coach or therapist, as well as following the other guidelines in this book.

So the point is to not use distraction as a solo strategy, but rather to go hand-in-hand with what you have already learned so far.

I'm going to share with you some ways that you can use distraction when tempted to engage in your usual eating disorder behaviors.

1. If you're tempted to binge-eat:

If you get the urge to binge-eat, convince yourself to 'delay' this behavior by doing something else instead. Examples are going for a walk, watching a video, or calling someone you enjoy talking to. Pick an activity that you know will help you feel good. You might become so distracted or engaged in something else that you end up feeling better afterwards, and the urge to binge-eat has already passed!

2. If you're tempted to over-exercise:

Once you've started applying what you've learned in Chapter 7, you'll begin to associate physical activity with joy, excitement, energy, self-care, and self-love. However, I personally understand that there are times you need tools to fall back on as you're healing.

If you feel tempted to over-exercise, decide to do something active but fun, something that is not going to feel like a 'chore' or like 'punishment.'

You can bargain with yourself that you're still doing something active, but with a different aim in mind. You will feel good afterwards because you did something that you enjoyed while still moving about. An example could be strolling through a shopping mall and browsing your favorite stores.

3. If you're tempted to purge:

Since purging usually happens right after eating or bingeing, create a distraction right after you've had your meals. This will remove the temptation or possibility of being able to purge what you just ate. For example, make a plan with a friend to go out and do something. Go for a walk, or go see a movie, anything that will get you out of the house and away from the bathroom.

There are many different things that you can do to distract yourself when your eating disorder thoughts become very strong, and when you feel the urge to act on them. I'd like to challenge you to create your own 'distraction list' of things that you like to do that you can have handy in those difficult times. Here is an example list:

- Meditate.

- Create art.

- Write in your journal.

- Do someone a favor.

- Bake something healthy and delicious.

- Read a book.

- Pray.

- Clean your apartment.

- Do a puzzle.

- Learn how to make your own lattes.

- Start researching something that fascinates you online.

These are just a few examples of distraction activities! Please take a moment to write a list of at least 10 activities that you personally enjoy and that you could see yourself using as distractions when you're having temptations to engage in eating disorder behaviors.

Opposite-Action

Doing the 'opposite-action' is a coping skill that was developed as part of DBT to help cope when faced with overwhelming emotions.[62]

When we feel a strong emotion (as you may have found from doing the self-monitoring activity), it usually urges us to want to act in a certain way.[62] For example, if you feel sad, you tend to want to withdraw and isolate yourself from others.

What DBT teaches is to do the opposite of what you feel urged to do! So, if you feel sad, instead of internalizing that sadness, seek others out.

This makes a lot of sense when you consider what you've already learned so far: that eating disorders thrive in isolation, and that social support can help protect you against developing mental illnesses, like eating disorders.

The purpose of this 'opposite action' activity is to help you try out behaviors that work and that are effective, and to experience how they compare to any current, unhelpful ones.

Mindfulness

Mindfulness is the ability to be present in any given moment. The point of practicing mindfulness is to enhance your self-awareness, to become more in touch with what you

---

[62] See Koonce (2018) for more information on how to apply opposite-actions.

are thinking, feeling, and sensing in your current environment. More importantly, it is also about accepting your thoughts and feelings, as 'bad' as they feel, without any attachment, and without analyzing or judging.[63] When you do this, you start to become more self-accepting, and more able to manage and sit with uncomfortable thoughts and emotions. Experiencing uncomfortable emotions is a part of life, and we all need to learn how to manage them in a way that honors us.

Mindfulness, as well as helping you to regulate your emotions and enhance your self-acceptance, can also help you become more in-tune with your body. Do you remember learning about mindful eating in the previous chapter? This is especially effective in helping you become more in-tune with your body, and in helping you to recognize hunger and satiation signals. To practice mindfulness, try the following activity:

---

[63] See Sanchez-Cordova (n.d.) for more information on mindfulness, including how to practice mindfulness.

Practice Being 'Still'

1. Set some time aside to practice being still, it could be just 5 minutes to start with.

2. Take some deep breaths in and out and just focus on your breathing: how it sounds, how it feels, just bring your attention to your breath.

3. If you feel your mind start to wander, just observe this, accept it, and gently bring your focus back to your breath.

This is a simple and short activity that won't take too much time out of your day, and which will get you started in learning how to be more mindful.

Self-Soothing

Self-soothing is a coping skill that you can use that can also help when you feel overcome by strong emotions. Self-soothing functions in much the same way as mindfulness in that it helps to bring you back to the present moment. It is especially useful if you have experienced trauma and tend to relive that trauma, and it can replace escape mechanisms like binge-eating and substance use.

The next time you feel overwhelmed with emotion and feel yourself tensing up, try to engage your five senses to bring your focus back to the present and away from the intense emotions. Self-soothing is the first thing I do when I experience feelings of panic and overwhelm. It's helpful because during these times, it's hard to even think straight. I calm myself down by soothing, and doing something like wrapping myself in a heated blanket, or putting one of my favorite shows on, or watching baby animal videos on Youtube. Next time you feel distressed, using your 5 senses, look around you and in your current environment. Name 5 things that you can see, 4 things that you can hear, 3 things that you can touch, 2 things that you can smell, and 1 thing that you can taste.

This is known as the 5-4-3-2-1 grounding technique and it is an effective way to calm yourself down when you feel an extreme rush of anxiousness or nervousness.[64]

---

[64] See Sherman Counseling (n.d.) for more information on grounding and how to practice it.

Breathwork

Breathwork can be considered a kind of mindfulness exercise too, where the aim is to focus on your breathing and being present while doing so.

Physiologically speaking, though, diaphragmatic breathing activates the parasympathetic nervous system, the calming one that helps lower the stress hormones, otherwise known as cortisol and adrenaline. It turns the fight or flight mechanism off by activating the diaphragmatic "phrenic" nerve to help send signals through the nervous system to the brain. A neurochemical reaction takes place in the body.

To practice diaphragmatic breathing, take a slow inhale breath in through your nose, allowing your stomach to rise. Then, slowly allow the breath to come out of your mouth by pursing your lips on exhalation. It takes practice to allow your stomach to rise because most of us are not accustomed to this breathing style and are used to shallow breathing through our mouths. Placing a hand on your stomach to connect with the feeling of allowing to rise with each breath can help. [65]

I know that these self-soothing type activities take time to learn and to get used to. A therapist once told me that we usually need self-soothing most when we feel our worst! That's the irony of it all: you usually don't feel like doing any of these activities because you are in a headspace where you just feel awful.

I'd like to reiterate just how powerful these practices are, though. It does take a few tries to engage your senses and do breathwork if you're new to it. You may even feel like it's not working at first, or that it doesn't help enough, but keep at it!

I can remember in my recovery from Binge-Eating Disorder, I had to practice getting in touch with these simple things and notice small things like my senses and how bringing my awareness to them made me feel. It was almost like I had ignored them before because I was so focused on myself and my eating disorder. So from a person who has

---

[65] See Cioffredi & Associates Physical Therapy (2012) for details on how to practice diaphragmatic breathing.

been there and kept at it, remember that self-soothing practices do often take time to appreciate and get used to.

Managing Triggers

If you completed the self-monitoring activity from chapter 1, then you might have an idea about what some of your 'triggers' are by now. A trigger is some situation, reminder, or thought that usually makes you feel a very strong emotion, and which can urge you to engage in your disordered eating behaviors.

If you know what your triggers are, then you can take steps to manage them better. That's why I spoke about self-awareness as such an important first step! Take a moment and think about what some of the things that trigger you may be and write them down.

Some examples could be comments on your weight, body, or food; weighing yourself; checking your body in the mirror regularly; and keeping old clothes that are too small for you and that no longer fit you, in the hopes that they one day will. Once you have come up with a list of some of your triggers, think about what you can do to manage them. Here are some examples:

1. Comments on your weight, body, or food.

If people comment on your weight, body or food, there are a couple of different ways you can respond. Remember, whatever people say to you about your weight, food, or body, they probably don't realize the impact that their words may have on you. It may seem like they are being rude or trying to hurt you, but this is usually not the case. What people say to you is always a reflection of what is going on with them, and represents their own views and biases. You can't control what people might say to you, but you can control how you respond. The way you respond to people's comments can help them realize that their comments are inappropriate and unhelpful.

If you don't want to engage with what someone has said to you, you can simply tell them that your body, weight, and what you eat is your business, and then you can quickly change the subject.[66]

For example, say someone notices that you have put on weight and tells you to watch your eating, you could tell them thanks, but that you know what is best for you[66]. They will probably feel a bit awkward and will not want to continue the conversation.

For people who you trust a bit more, you can explain just how uncomfortable their comments make you feel and about how their comments have a negative impact on your recovery and can set you back.[66] You can also guide them on what kind of support and encouragement would be best for you.

For example, a loved one telling you that you have gained weight may have a positive intention behind it. They may want you to know that they are happy to see you getting better. You can gently tell them that these kinds of comments are not helpful, and tell them how you'd like to be supported instead, for example, that you'd prefer comments on how you are doing better internally.[66] Follow the Intuition (2020)[62] lists several 'typical' comments that you may get during your recovery and provides some back-up responses that you can use if these come up.

Have a look at the below comments and responses taken directly from Follow the Intuition (2020):

---

[66] See "Follow the Intuition" (2020) for more suggestions on how to handle comments on your weight, shape, and eating habits.

Comment: "You've gained some weight, you should watch what you're eating."[62]

Response: "My body, my business."[62]

Comment: "You should probably start working out more."[62]

Response: "I know what is best for me but thank you."[62]

Comment: "I wouldn't eat that much of x because it's a lot of fat/carbs/calories."[62]

Response: "So don't. I know what is best for me."[62]

These kinds of responses quickly shut down any further conversation around food and eating, and allow you to take control by changing the subject, and asserting yourself.

2. Weighing Yourself

If you have a scale accessible at home and you are tempted to weigh yourself often, you could remove and get rid of the batteries in it and put it somewhere out of sight, such as inside a cupboard. There are times in an eating disorder where the scale is a metric for letting you know "how good you're doing", or if you ate the "right" foods, or if you're "on track". I now give you permission to stop thinking of the scale as a way to signal virtue, and begin incorporating a different habit, such as regular movement, or eating a variety of nutrient-dense foods daily, as a way to feel like you're on the right track with your health.

Weighing yourself often is typical behavior when you have an eating disorder, but your weight can fluctuate so much throughout a single day or week for various reasons. For example, your weight may go up or down throughout the day and week depending on your food and water intake, stress, or from muscles retaining water as they heal post-workout. So when you weigh yourself throughout the day, you will not get an accurate picture of whether you have lost or gained weight. Are you beginning to see how assigning value, beauty, goodness and worth based on the scale number wastes our energy? It can feel like an emotional roller coaster. A concept that helped me get over the scale was beginning to think of my body as a genius, complex structure that knows what it's doing. I know that this might be difficult and you may not want to shift away from weighing yourself, but it's more helpful if we can change our focus onto feeling good in recovery. The scale does not determine your worth, and can rob you of feeling good.

If you're visiting the doctor and they ask you to step on the scale, you can simply ask not to be weighed. Casually asking, "can we skip that today?" usually goes over well. If they insist, you can tell them that you're in eating disorder recovery and struggle with body image. The person checking you in will likely understand and move onto the next thing. Another technique you can use if you decide to allow a weight is to step on the scale backwards so you don't see the numbers. Tell the person weighing you not to tell you your weight or let you see the number.

3. Body Checking

Checking how your body looks in the mirror on a regular basis is another common eating disorder behavior that is as unhelpful as frequently weighing yourself. It causes you to become hypercritical and hypersensitive to any perceived changes in your body size, and it can send you into a downward spiral of obsession. The self-judgement and negative emotions that come with that is enough to ruin your day sometimes

So, if you have any mirrors - especially full-length mirrors - that are movable, a good idea during recovery could be to remove or hide them, so that it's not as easy to constantly check your body.

One way to shift your worth off of the way your body looks in the mirror is to begin focusing on the quality of your character. What makes you, *you*? What do people love about you? You'll find that asking this question reminds you that people don't like you because of the way your body looks. For example, they want to be friends with you and spend time with you because you make them feel good, loved, and seen! Eating disorder recovery requires that we learn the truth about ourselves, and how amazing we are outside of appearance.

4. Letting go of the past

If you have been holding on to a past version of yourself, perhaps a 'smaller,' younger version of yourself, then it is time to let that old version of yourself go.

What is the point of holding on to those jeans from high school, or even that wedding dress from 5 years ago? Who are you trying to fit into for that? Does it really matter? What changes if you fit into that? Will it solve your problems? Chances are you will be in the same mental place that you are right now, not fitting into it.

Create different, better, more high-reaching goals for yourself. Not goals that drag you into the past and that don't truly mean anything about you.

Chapter 12

Enhance Your Confidence, Self -Esteem & Body-Image

If you take anyone with an eating disorder and you assess them on their confidence, self-esteem and body-image, you can almost guarantee that they will score very low on these different dimensions. We've previously covered how low self-esteem and body-image dissatisfaction are massive risk factors for the development of eating disorders.

So, if having low self-esteem, low confidence and poor body-image contribute to the development of eating disorders and keep them going, then these areas are crucial to work on in order to heal and make a full recovery.

In this final chapter, you'll learn about how low confidence, low self-esteem, and poor body-image function in eating disorders. I'll also share some tips and practical activities to get you started on building up these different areas.

Confidence: What is it and How is it Developed?

Confidence can be defined as "the feeling or belief that you can do something well or succeed at something."[67]

As someone with an eating disorder, you probably set high standards for yourself, or believe that others expect a lot from you. Usually, these standards are unrealistic and near impossible to attain, so when you 'fail' to reach them, your confidence takes a hit.

That's how eating disorders pull people with low confidence in. The thought of being able to control at least something - your eating, your body - is appealing. If you succeed at reaching some weight or body-related goal, you may get a small confidence boost, especially if others notice. But often, it is short-lived, as there always seems to be a new goal to reach, so you never feel good enough.

---

[67] See Merriam-Webster (n.d.) for further information on the definition of confidence.

Real confidence is built when you make space for opportunities that will give you a sense of accomplishment in aspects of your life other than your appearance. It is also about becoming comfortable with 'failure' and facing your fears head-on.

Facing your fears can be especially intimidating when you have a very harsh inner critic. Something that can help, is to break your biggest fears down into smaller 'steps' that you need to surpass in order to fully overcome them.

The Fear Ladder

A fear ladder is often used in the treatment of anxiety or phobias. It is used to help people take small steps towards overcoming their biggest fears. It works to help people break their fear down into smaller 'steps' that seem more manageable. Now, imagine a ladder. Think about something that causes you a lot of anxiety, that you feel you are not really capable of, which if you proved yourself wrong, could help boost your confidence! For example, let's say you have difficulty making friends, or you don't feel that you are capable of making them. Now, let's think about the steps that you need to take in order to make friends, and rank how 'scary' these steps may be to you on a scale of 1 - 10, with 1 being not scary at all, and 10 being extremely frightening.

1) Saying hello to someone you have never met before (6/10).

2) Making small talk with someone new (7/10).

3) Sharing contact details with someone you just met (8/10).

4) Inviting someone you just met to spend time with you (9/10).

5) Sharing personal information to get closer to someone (10/10).

Give this activity a try using the situation that you thought of, that gives you a lot of anxiety and that you feel incapable at.

Now that you have written down the 'steps' that go with your own example, and have ranked them, go ahead and draw a ladder. Write each of the steps above the ladder rungs. It will look a little like this:

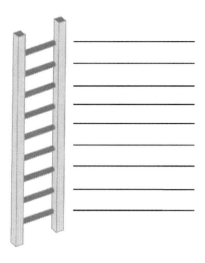

Figure 2

Starting at the bottom rung of the ladder, set yourself a goal only for step number 1, for example:

"I will say hello to someone new everyday." Give yourself a new fear rating each time you practice this step, until you score an anxiety level of 2 or 3.

Once you have mastered the first step, you can move on and set a goal for step 2, and keep going like this until you have reached the final step.

This activity is just one of many ways that you can start to rebuild confidence in yourself and in your capabilities: as you start to accomplish what you thought was impossible, your belief in yourself will grow tremendously. Getting out of your comfort zone creates personal expansion, increases your self- esteem and how good you feel about yourself. This is SO important for personal happiness and satisfaction in life!

Self-Esteem

Self-esteem and self-confidence often get mixed up, and are sometimes even used interchangeably. The main difference between the two is that self-confidence has more to do with the belief in your abilities and being able to do things well. Whereas self-esteem has more to do with what you believe about yourself as a whole, and how you value your worth as a person.

We've talked about some of the ways in which you can enhance your self-esteem in the previous chapter. These include reframing your core beliefs about yourself, practicing positive affirmations, and setting attainable goals. Having a low view of yourself often arises from your core beliefs, which are deeply entrenched and which take time and conscious effort to change. That is why it is critical to practice reframing negative beliefs about yourself and repeating positive self-affirmations regularly, too. Setting and achieving goals helps reinforce the idea that you can do what you set your mind to! In the next exercise, the idea is to get you thinking about the strengths that you already possess, and that having low self-esteem makes it easy to forget.

This practice comes from the narrative therapy tradition, which helps people reconstruct their experiences and see them from a different, and positive perspective.[68] Begin by thinking about a time where you felt really proud in your life. It could be, for example, a difficult situation that you overcame in your life, or something that made you feel accomplished.

Now, write about that experience, all while emphasizing your strengths and values. Also write about any emotions you felt, or if there were others involved, how they must have felt too. When you have finished writing about your experience, go back and underline phrases or words that you feel really speak to your strengths.

---

[68] See Ackerman (2021) for more information on narrative therapy.

Then, write out a list of your strengths that you can come back to at times where you feel worthless, or when your eating disorder thoughts become loud and critical.

Body-Image

In eating disorder recovery, body-image issues are often the last to be resolved. You can recover physically from your eating disorder but still struggle to accept your body fully.

What makes this especially difficult is how we are constantly inundated with messages of what we should look like every single day. They are impossible to get away from! That is why it is so important to build up your self-esteem and self-confidence, especially in those non-physical aspects of yourself.

Improving your body-image is about learning self-acceptance, and is about seeing your body as more than just how it looks to others on the outside. It is an inevitable fact of life that our bodies will change and adapt as we go through different phases of life. Age, stress, hormones, and childbearing make our bodies susceptible to change, but if we can appreciate our bodies for that very adaptability, we can develop a different kind of love and respect for them. When you think negative thoughts about how you look, you're sending your mind and cells a powerful message. Our cells have vibrational energy, and negative thoughts and emotions affect the vibration and functioning of our cells. We must remember that maintaining a negative perspective about ourselves and our bodies affects its cellular makeup and quality. Negativity can contribute to internal stress, sickness and disease. We benefit from speaking loving and positive words over ourselves. It never seems to come naturally, but your life and livelihood depends on it.

For example, right now, try to make a list of all the things that you are grateful for about your body.

Here is my list:

- My body keeps me alive everyday without me having to even think about how.

- My body has the capacity to be a home for a baby.

- My body allows me to move, dance and travel places.

- My body is strong.

You can also create affirmations about your body that you'd like to believe about your body but that you don't believe yet. For example:

- I love my body.

- I am not just my body, there is more to life than my weight.

- I nourish my body with healthy and delicious foods.

- I treat my body with love and respect.

- My body has been perfectly created.

Your turn! Write at least 5 things that you'd like to believe about your body. The best way to start healing your relationship with your body, is to view yourself through a lens of love, compassion and gratitude.

Leave a 1-Click Review!

It would mean the world to me if you took 60 seconds to leave this book a brief review on Amazon, even if it is just a few sentences!

>>Click here to leave a quick review

Conclusion

I pray that this book has inspired you, encouraged you and given you hope that eating disorder recovery is not only possible, but that your future is bright and rich in happiness.

Eating disorders and health are not mutually exclusive, and this book is meant to bridge that gap. For the longest time, I didn't know how to pursue a healthy life and recover from my eating disorder. I used to think that I couldn't trust my body to manage my weight. I believed the lie that I would have to be the one to control it and "make it behave" with disordered eating behaviors.

Each chapter of this book is important in its own way, and the chapters were carefully ordered to represent this. Now you can see why I asked you to read the book in order without skipping around!

We first had to address eating disorders by looking at their cause and how they are maintained, so that you could better understand your own eating disorder: why and how it developed and how it had functioned in your life. Through self-monitoring, you learned that self-awareness is a great first step in recovery because when you are self-aware, you know what needs to change and can make progress towards resolving problems.

Before we got into any other strategies and techniques, we needed to address your mindset. You were made aware of the fact that, to set yourself up successfully for recovery, you needed to start by committing to recovery and all that it entails, being fully alert to the various challenges.

Then, it was a matter of introducing healthful habits that helped you snowball towards recovery, one step at a time. You also learned about different social support resources, and about how important it is to connect with others, be that professionals, like psychologists, community support groups, and friends and family. You found out what it means to be 'spiritual,' that you could develop your spiritual side even if you don't believe in God, or any higher power. You learned the value this could bring in helping to forge your identity. You developed a knowledge foundation for basic and holistic nutrition, which helped you understand the benefits to eating a healthy, balanced diet that sufficiently meets your body's needs. You were taught how to re-imagine nutrition and physical activity, and about the role of each as part of a healthy lifestyle.

For sustained recovery and relapse prevention, you were provided with effective coping strategies for managing your triggers, and you were given tools to enhance your self-esteem, confidence, and body-image.

Eating disorders are complex, which is why a multi-faceted, holistic approach to recovery that addresses all areas of your life is so important, and is the key to lasting recovery.

Sincerely,

About the Author

Kara Holmes is a Registered Nurse & eating disorder recovery coach. After healing from her own eating disorder of 11 years, she now helps determined women struggling with eating disorders find holistic healing and recovery by teaching them how to listen to their bodies and reimagine food, weight, and body image. She is passionate about holistic health, finding true balance in all areas of life, and inviting God into each experience. In her free time, she enjoys long hikes in the wilderness, creating new recipes in her kitchen, and traveling to new cities.

Did you get your recovery bonus that comes with your purchase?

You can get your copy of *"7 Hacks for Learning to Eat Without Fear of Weight Gain"* at my website: 'bonusguide.vitalitycoaching.org'

I'd love to meet you! Here are a few ways to stay connected:

Subscribe to my Eating Disorder Recovery Podcast, _The Stress-Free Living Show_ (available on all the podcasting platforms) and get unmissable weekly tips, guest interviews, and support in your recovery journey!

Instagram: @itskaraleighann

Join Our Eating Disorder Support Tribe on Facebook:
https://www.facebook.com/groups/eatingdisorderrecoverytribe

Book a free 1:1 coaching session with me:
www.vitalitycoaching.org/coaching-program/

Questions? Send me a message on IG or at
www.vitalitycoaching.org!

References

Ackerman, C.E. (2021, 25 November). 18 Self-Esteem Worksheets and Activities for Teens and Adults. *PositivePsychology.com.* https://positivepsychology.com/self-esteem-worksheets/

American Heart Association. (2020, November 6). What is Cholesterol? *American Heart Association.* https://www.heart.org/en/health-topics/cholesterol/about-cholesterol

Baker, D., & Keramides, N. (2013). The Psychology of Hunger. *Monitor on Psychology, 44*(9), 66.

Beauregard, M. (2014). Functional Neuroimaging Studies of the Effects of Psychotherapy. *Dialogues in Clinical Neuroscience, 16*(1), 75-81. doi: 10.31887/DCNS.2014.16.1/mbeauregard

Bjarnadottir, A. (2017). Why Refined Carbs are Bad for You. *Healthline.* https://www.healthline.com/nutrition/why-refined-carbs-are-bad#TOC_TITLE_HDR_2

Bolt, B. (2015, June 22). Vitamins and Minerals Explained. *Pharmacy Times.* https://www.pharmacytimes.com/view/vitamins-and-minerals-explained

Brennan, D. (2021, January 21). How Would you Know if a Person has Scurvy? *Medicine Net.* https://www.medicinenet.com/how_would_you_know_if_a_person_has_scurvy/article.htm

Centre for Clinical Interventions (2021). Module 4: Self-Monitoring in Eating Disorders. *Government of Western Australia.* https://www.cci.health.wa.gov.au/~/media/CCI/Consumer-Modules/Overcoming-Disordered-Eating---Part-A/Overcoming-Disordered-Eating---04---Self-monitoring.pdf

Cherry, K., & Morin, A. (2021, April 8). What is Self-Esteem? *VeryWellMind.*

https://www.verywellmind.com/what-is-self-esteem-2795868

Cioffredi & Associates Physical Therapy. (2021, August 22). Learn the Diaphragmatic Breathing Technique. [Video]. Youtube. https://www.youtube.com/watch?v=kgTL5G1ibIo

Clear, J. (n.d.). How Long Does it Actually Take to Form a New Habit? (Backed by Science). *James Clear.* https://jamesclear.com/new-habit

Clifford & Kozil. (n.d.). Fat-Soluble Vitamins A, D, E, and K. *Colorado State University.* https://extension.colostate.edu/topic-areas/nutrition-food-safety-health/fat-soluble-vitamins-a-d-e-and-k-9-315/

Costin, C. (2020). Comparing the Two Types of Support: Therapy and Coaching. *Carolyn Costin.* https://www.carolyn-costin.com/copy-of-what-does-an-ed-coach-do

Cowden, S. (2020). Dialectical Behavior Therapy for Eating Disorders. *Very Well Mind.*

https://www.verywellmind.com/dialectical-behavior-therapy-for-eating-disorders-1138350

Crum, A.J., Salovey, P., & Achor, S. (2013). Rethinking Stress: The Role of Mindsets in Determining the Stress Response. *Journal of Personality and Social Psychology, 104*(4), 716 - 733.doi: 10.1037/a0031201

Dansinger, M. (2021). How to Use the Glycemic Index. *Webmd.* https://www.webmd.com/diabetes/guide/glycemic-index-good-versus-bad-carbs

Dientsman, A. M. (2019). 8 Simple, Everyday Spiritual Practice Ideas. *Goodnet.* https://www.goodnet.org/articles/8-simple-everyday-spiritual-practice-ideas

Dietary Guidelines for Americans. (2010). Estimated Calorie Needs Per Day by Age, Gender, and Physical Activity [PDF]. https://extension.colostate.edu/docs/smallsteps/calorie-needs.pdf

Doran, G. T. (1981). There's a S.M.A.R.T. Way to Write Management's Goals and Objectives, *Management Review*, 70(11), 35-36.

Duckworth, A. [TED]. (2021, April 30). The Strongest Predictor for Success | Angela Lee Duckworth [Video]. Youtube. https://www.youtube.com/watch?v=GfF2e0vyGM4

Eating Disorder Hope (2018, February 2018). ACT & Eating Disorder Treatment: What you Need to Know. *Eating Disorder Hope.* https://www.eatingdisorderhope.com/blog/act-ed-treatment

Ekern, J. & Karges, C.(2012). Eating Disorders and Addiction: Why we Continue to Engage in Self-Destructive Behaviors. *Eating Disorder Hope.* https://www.eatingdisorderhope.com/treatment-for-eating-disorders/co-occurring-dual-diagnosis/alcohol-substance-abuse/eating-disorders-and-addiction-why-we-continue-to-engage-in-self-destructive-behaviors

Elliot, B. (2021). 14 Reasons Why You're Always Hungry. *Healthline.*

https://www.healthline.com/nutrition/14-reasons-always-hungry#3.-Youre-eating-too-many-refined-carb

EMDR Institute. (n.d.). What is EMDR? https://www.emdr.com/what-is-emdr/

Engel, G.L. (1977). The Need for a New Medical Model: a Challenge for Biomedicine. *Psychodynamic Psychiatry, 40*(3), 377 - 396. doi: 10.1126/science.847460

Follow the Intuition. (2020, April 21). How to Respond to Triggering Comments in Eating Disorder Recovery. https://followtheintuition.com/how-to-respond-to-triggering-comments/

Fursland, A., Byrne, S. & Nathan, P. (2007). Overcoming Disordered Eating: Module 4 Self-Monitoring. *Centre for Clinical Interventions.* https://www.cci.health.wa.gov.au/~/media/CCI/Consumer-Modules/Overcoming-Disordered-Eating---Part-A/Overcoming-Disordered-Eating---04---Self-monitoring.pdf

Ghaderi, A., & Scott, B. (2001). Prevalence, Incidence and Prospective Risk Factors for Eating Disorders. *Acta Psychiatrica Scandinavica, 104*(2), 122 - 130. doi: 10.1034/j.1600-0447.2001.00298.x

Gil, C. (n.d.). *The Starvation Experiment*. DukeHealth. https://eatingdisorders.dukehealth.org/education/res ources/starvation-experiment

Harlow H. F., Dodsworth R. O., & Harlow M. K. (1965). Total Social Isolation in Monkeys. Proceedings of the National Academy of Sciences of the United States of America. https://www.ncbi.nlm.nih.gov/pmc/articles/PMC28 5801/pdf/pnas00159-0105.pdf

Harlow HF. (1958). The Nature of Love. *American Psychologist,* 13(12), 673-685. doi:10.1037/h0047884

Harlow, H.F., Suomi, S.J. (1971). Social Recovery by Isolation-Reared Monkeys. *Proceedings of the National Academy of Sciences of the United States of America, 68*(7), 1534–1538.

Harris, R.B. (2015). Chronic and Acute Effects of Stress on Energy Balance: Are There Appropriate Animal Models? *American Journal of Physiology: Regulatory, Integrative and Comparative Physiology, 308*(4), 250 - 265. doi: 10.1152/ajpregu.00361.2014

Hill, N. (n.d.). 4 Ways Spirituality Can Help and Hinder Eating Disorder Recovery. *Walden Behavioral Care.* https://www.waldeneatingdisorders.com/blog/4-ways-spirituality-can-help-and-hinder-eating-disorder-recovery/

Horvath, A. O. (2001). The Alliance. *Psychotherapy: Theory, Research, Practice, Training, 38*(4), 365–372. https://doi.org/10.1037/0033-3204.38.4.365

IBISWorld. (2021). Weight Loss Services in the US - Market Size 2002 - 2027. *IBISWorld.* https://www.ibisworld.com/industry-statistics/market-size/weight-loss-services-united-states/

Jacobson, S. (2019, September 22). Cognitive Distortions (Thinking Errors). *Harley Therapy: Psychotherapy and Counselling in London.*

https://www.harleytherapy.co.uk/cognitive-distortions-cbt.htm

Koonce, D. (2018, June 3). Using Opposite Action for Overwhelming Emotions. *Mindsoother Therapy Center.* https://www.mindsoother.com/blog/using-opposite-action-for-overwhelming-emotions

Mayo Clinic. (n.d.). Trans Fat is Double Trouble for your Heart Health. *Mayo Clinic.* https://www.mayoclinic.org/diseases-conditions/high-blood-cholesterol/in-depth/trans-fat/art-20046114#:~:text=Trans%20fat%20increases%20your%20LDL,your%20brain%2C%20causing%20a%20stroke.

Mejia, Z. (2017, November 21). Harvard Researchers say that this Mental Shift will make you Live a Longer, Healthier Life. *Make it.* https://www.cnbc.com/2017/11/21/harvard-researchers-say-a-purpose-leads-to-longer-healthier-life.html

Merriam-Webster. (n.d.). Confidence. https://www.merriam-webster.com/dictionary/confidence

Murphy, R., Straebler, S., Cooper, Z., & Fairburn, C. (2010). Cognitive Behavioral Therapy for Eating Disorders. *Psychiatric Clinics of North America, 33*(3), 611 - 627. doi:10.1016/j.psc.2010.04.004

National Institutes of Health (2007, April 12). Analysis of Rhesus Monkey Genome Uncovers Genetic Differences With Humans, Chimps. *US Department of Health and Human Services.* https://www.nih.gov/news-events/news-releases/analysis-rhesus-monkey-genome-uncovers-genetic-differences-humans-chimps

Nortje, A. (2021, November 25). Social Comparison: An Unavoidable Upward or Downward Spiral. *PositivePsychology.com.* https://positivepsychology.com/social-comparison/

Ozbay, F., Johnson, D.C., Dimoulas, E., Morgan, C.A., Charney, D., & Southwick, S. (2007). Social Support and Resilience to Stress: From Neurobiology to

Clinical Practice. *Psychiatry (Edgemont), 45*(5), 35 - 40.

NHLBI. (n.d.). Calculate Your Body Mass Index. https://www.nhlbi.nih.gov/health/educational/lose_ wt/BMI/bmi-m.htm

Pillay, S. (2011, November 17). The Science of Visualization: Maximizing Your Brain's Potential During The Recession. *Huffpost.* https://www.huffpost.com/entry/the-science-of-visualizat_b_171340

Powell, L. H., Kazlauskaite, R., Shima, C., & Appelhans, B. M. (2010). Lifestyle in France and the United States: an American perspective. *Journal of the American Dietetic Association, 110*(6), 845–847. doi: https://doi.org/10.1016/j.jada.2010.03.029

Reachout.com (n.d.). What is Spirituality? https://www.ideas.org.au/uploads/resources/550/Wh at%20Is%20Spirituality.pdf

Roberts, D. (2018, August 27). Luck, Success and the Fundamental Attribution Error. *Abnormal Returns.*

https://abnormalreturns.com/2018/08/27/luck-success-and-the-fundamental-attribution-error/

Rubin, C. (2011, August 23). The Route to Happiness: Set Ambitious Goals , says a Study. *Inc.* https://www.inc.com/news/articles/201108/study-says-ambitious-goals-make-people-happier.html

Sanchez-Cordova. (n.d.). Practicing Mindfulness and Positive Coping Strategies. *Beach Psychology, Hermosa Beach CA.* https://www.dr-kellywarren.com/single-post/2017/01/18/practicing-mindfulness-and-positive-coping-strategies

Sherman Counseling. (n.d.). How to Ground Yourself During an Anxiety Attack | Anxiety Treatment Wisconsin. https://www.shermanconsulting.net/2018/06/05/grounding-methods-anxiety-attacks/

Soots, L (2015, August). What are Habits? *The Positive Psychology People.* https://www.thepositivepsychologypeople.com/habits-to-happiness/

Spritzler, F., & Arnarson, A. (2019, November 7). How Cooking Affects the Nutrient Content of Foods. *Healthline.* https://www.healthline.com/nutrition/cooking-nutrient-content#:~:text=Because%20vitamin%20C%20is%20water,and%20its%20juices%20run%20off.

Tinsley, G & Felman, A. (2020). Is Saturated or Unsaturated Fat Better for Health? *Medical News Today.* https://www.medicalnewstoday.com/articles/32165 5

Tomiyama, A. J., Mann, T., Vinas, D., Hunger, J. M., Dejager, J., & Taylor, S. E. (2010). Low Calorie Dieting Increases Cortisol. *Psychosomatic Medicine, 72*(4), 357 - 364. doi: 10.1097/PSY.0b013e3181d9523c

Vitousek, K. M., & Brown, K. E. (2015). Cognitive-Behavioural Theory of Eating Disorders. The Wiley Handbook of Eating Disorders, 222-237. doi: 10.1002/9781118574089.ch18

Warley, S. (n.d.). Find your Why to get Unstuck. *Life Skills that Matter*. https://lifeskillsthatmatter.com/find-your-why/

Washington State University (n.d.). *Nutrition Basics*. https://mynutrition.wsu.edu/nutrition-basics

Printed in Great Britain
by Amazon